DEVELOPING
ORGANIZATION
ETHICS
IN HEALTHCARE

DEVELOPING ORGANIZATION ETHICS IN HEALTHCARE

A Case-Based Approach to Policy, Practice, and Compliance

Edited by Ann E. Mills,
Edward M. Spencer,
and Patricia H. Werhane

University Publishing Group
Hagerstown, Maryland

University Publishing Group, Inc.
Hagerstown, Maryland 21740
1-800-654-8188
www.upgbooks.com

Copyright © 2001 by University Publishing Group
All rights reserved. No part of this publication may be reproduced,
stored in a retrieval system, or transmitted, in any form, or by any
means, electronic, mechanical, photocopying, recording or otherwise,
without the prior permission of University Publishing Group.
Printed in the United States of America

ISBN 1-55572-064-1

Appendix D, "Making the Most of Disequiliburium: Bridging the Gap
Between Clinical and Organizational Ethics in a Newly Merged Healthcare
Organization," by Catherine Myser, Patricia Doenhower, and Cathy Frank, first
appeared in *The Journal of Clinical Ethics* 9, no. 4 (Winter 1998); © 1998 by
The Journal of Clinical Ethics; used with permission.

Appendix E, "Fulfilling Institutional Responsibilities in Healthcare:
Organizational Ethics and the Role of Mission Discernment," by John A.
Gallagher and Jerry Goodstein, is a version of an article that will appear in
Business Ethics Quarterly, © 2001, *Business Ethics Quarterly;* used with its
kind permission.

Appendix F-1, Principles of Medical Ethics, American Medical
Association, © 2000; used with its kind permission.

Appendix F-2, Code of Ethics for Nurses, American Nurses Association,
© 2001; used with its kind permission.

Appendix F-3, Code of Ethics, Healthcare Information and Management
System Society, © 2001; used with its kind permission.

Appendix F-4, Consensus Statement on the Ethic of Medicine, Council of
Medical Specialties Societies, © 2001; used with its kind permission.

Appendix F-5, Declaration of Helsinki, World Medical Association,
© 2001; used with its kind permission.

Appendix F-6, Code of Ethics, American College of Healthcare
Executives, © 2001; used with its kind permission.

Contents

Part Three:
Organization Issues in Professional Ethics

Part Four:
Organization Issues in Research Ethics

Appendixes

Acknowledgments

We extend our thanks to Jonathan D. Moreno, Director of the University of Virginia's Center for Biomedical Ethics, and R. Edward Freeman, Director of the Olsson Center at University of Virginia's Darden Graduate School of Business Administration, for their encouragement and support.

We also thank Carrie Gumm, Project Support Technician, Senior, for employing her organizational skills on our behalf, and Henry Tulloch for editorial advice. Most particularly, we thank our contributors for their time in developing the cases presented in this book. They believe, as we do, that healthcare organization ethics has an important (perhaps the *most* important) role in delivery of care.

We are grateful to the professional societies that permitted us to include their codes of ethics: the American Medical Association, the American Nurses Association, the Healthcare Information and Managment Systems Society, the Council of Medical Specialties Societies, the World Medical Association, and the American College of Healthcare Executives.

Introduction

Ann E. Mills, Edward M. Spencer, and Patricia H. Werhane

This book presents a series of cases concerning ethical issues in healthcare organizations (HCOs). Organizations now dominate the delivery of care. The physician-entrepreneur model of healthcare delivery that has been supported by the medical establishment through much of its history in the United States is being replaced. Population groups—not individual patients—are now the focus of the healthcare delivery system, and population groups are more efficiently served through organizations than through individuals. Now, it is within an organizational setting that most healthcare delivery occurs. Yet there are few books that deal specifically with the ethical implications of organizational issues in healthcare, and there are no casebooks that focus directly on the organizational aspects of healthcare ethics. This book intends to remedy that situation.

Healthcare organization ethics is concerned with the ethical climate of an HCO and the effects of that climate on an organization itself and its associated stakeholders—notably, patients, clinicians, administrators, staff, contractual partners, and the community that is served by the organization. Healthcare organization ethics consists of the ideals and mechanisms that comprise the ethical climate of an HCO. It is manifested in the relationships among the individuals and groups who have a stake in an organization and its operation and the effect of those relationships on patient care.

Healthcare organization ethics owes its inception to the 1995 mandate of the Joint Commission on Accreditation of Healthcare Organizations (JCAHO) that requires HCOs to implement an organization ethics function. This function has to do with the ethical responsibility of the organization itself "to conduct its business and patient care practices in an honest, decent and proper manner."[1] A broader, more process-oriented definition of healthcare organization ethics has been advanced by the Virginia Bioethics Network (renamed the Virginia Healthcare Ethics Network, VHEN, in 1998): "Organization ethics consists of [a set of] processes to address ethical issues associated with the business, financial, and management areas of healthcare organizations, as well as with professional, educational, and contractual relationships affecting the operation of the HCO" (see appendix A for a complete text of the VHEN organization ethics guidelines).[2] These processes include articulation, application, and evaluation of the organization's mission and values statements. This definition demands that organization ethics activities encompass all aspects of the operation of an HCO so that a positive ethical climate can be developed and maintained. Because this definition of organization ethics encompasses all aspects of the operation of an HCO, it necessarily embraces all relationships having to do with healthcare delivery and has the potential to change or influence the other entities in the system, particularly managed-care organizations.

Interest in the way in which organizations behave is not new. Beginning shortly after the Watergate scandal, governmental "watchdog" agencies as well as private groups have shown an increasing interest in how corporations address legal issues. In 1991 this interest resulted in an extension of the Federal Sentencing Guidelines, and these guidelines were applied to organizations found guilty of violating federal law.[3] Because sentences and fines under these guidelines can be mitigated when the guilty organization can demonstrate that it has in place a "systematic and visible program within the organization which seeks to deter and prevent criminal activity,"[4] most corporations—including HCOs—have begun such activities under the rubric of "corporate compliance programs" or "ethics programs."

The intent of the Federal Sentencing Guidelines is to provide systematic punishment for those individuals or organizations that commit crimes, and an obvious intent of corporate compliance/ethics programs is to help an organization to avoid punishment for intentional or unintentional wrongdoing. An organization's obligation to obey the law may be the first step in building an appropriate ethical climate for the organization. But this obligation does not, in and of itself, develop, enhance, and promote an organization's positive ethical climate, which is comprised of the shared perceptions of the "general and pervasive characteristics of [an] organization [or a system] affecting a broad range of decisions."[5] The ethical climate of an organization defines it in both its internal and external relationships. An ethical climate is articulated via value statements; mission statements; organization codes of ethics; policies addressing specific ethical issues; and, most importantly, its effect on the attitudes and activities of everyone associated with the organization. It is built on the core values of an organization, which are the values or attributes by which an organization fulfills its mission. By definition, core values are relatively enduring through time. These are the values that define an organization's uniqueness, irrespective of strategic or structural changes. Thus, the concerns of healthcare organization ethics go beyond the requirement that the organization must seek to ensure that its agents act legally. The cases we have chosen for inclusion in this book are not about right and wrong in a criminal or legal sense, but about whether and how an organization lives up to its own ideals, how it communicates its expectations, and whether and how it develops or fails to develop internal mechanisms to fulfill its obligations.

We have only included cases where there is some commitment from HCO leaders to an articulated and positive ethical climate. The activities of any single person or committee aimed at developing, enhancing, and maintaining a positive ethical climate in an HCO are ineffective in the absence of clear organizational articulation of, and commitment to, an organization's core values at all levels, particularly the highest levels. For instance, consider the ten-year saga of the Allegheny Health System in Pennsylvania. Sherif S. Abdulhak, chief executive officer (CEO) and president, led organization leaders via a strategy that focused on aggressive expansion at whatever cost to its stakeholders. This strategy eventually resulted in the collapse of the Allegheny Health System, the firing of top and many mid-level executives (including Adbulhak), the restructuring of the board, the loss of thousands of jobs, the collapse of valuable community healthcare resources, and public condemnation and distrust of a once-venerable institution.[6]

Could organization ethics activities have made any difference to the outcomes experienced by the Allegheny Health System? The answer is probably no. Abdulhak, the board, and key organizational leaders (mostly recruited by Abdulhak and paid many times the national average) seemed focused solely on creating their vision of Allegheny, a large and lucrative healthcare system whose very existence seemed justified because of the benefits that accrued to key managers and certain physicians. They maintained this vision in spite of conflicts of interest, clearly defined and recognized ethically problematic processes, and growing media and community concern over wasteful management practices and the system's nonprofit status. They pursued this vision with an arrogance that bordered on disdain for Allegheny's most important stakeholders—its patients. In such an organization, any organization ethics activities to develop or enhance an ethical climate would have been ignored. Cases such as this are not helpful to persons seriously interested in developing, articulating, and enhancing an organization's ethical climate, who have the support of their organization to do so, even if the organization is uncertain about its strategic direction.

We start with the thesis that the use of case studies is the best pedagogical method to teach healthcare organization ethics. Bioethics and clinical ethics—as well as law and business[7]— have traditionally used the case method for teaching, illustration, and research. More importantly, there is growing evidence that experts acquire much of their knowledge through cases and examples.[8] James Rest's extensive research concludes that moral reasoning skills can be taught to adults and that skills are best taught through the case method.[9] We expose students to real-life situations that illustrate some particular set of issues and ask them to develop criteria for reasoning though these dilemmas that takes into account appropriate ethical and organizational concerns.

The cases we present have been collected from practicing professionals, clinicians, scholars, and students throughout the country. They are drawn from "real life" through news reports and from personal experience. To be inclusive and comprehensive, we have included cases relating to the activities of patients, clinicians, administrators, managers, and other individuals or groups both within and outside HCOs. These cases should be of interest to healthcare decision makers, as well as observers and students of the healthcare industry. Although this book primarily focuses on provider HCOs, many of the cases aptly apply to issues in managed care as well.

Most of the cases we have chosen are brief. We have chosen to eschew long and complicated cases—so-called full-length cases. Full-length cases are often used so that students may learn to distinguish which details are important and which are not in formulating and designing solutions to a particular dilemma. They often include the history, the background, and other contextual factors of the organization, its environment, and the persons involved in the particular dilemma. Full-length cases are generally drawn from different industries, whose organizations have substantially different missions and are often used together to illustrate common points of law or business or engineering. Here we are concerned with one industry and one organization within that industry.

The critical mission of HCOs is the care of patients. This is the justification of HCOs and, indeed, the justification of the whole of the healthcare delivery system. Thus, the missions of various and diverse HCOs are similar. The professional roles and responsibilities of various staff and clinicians within HCOs are also similar, so there is no need to detail the history and background of the various HCOs and actors in these organizations unless the case under review is substantially affected by the particular organization's history and background.

Further, we have for many years taught healthcare clinicians and healthcare managers. It is our experience that these persons want to get to the point quickly—without fuss or distraction. Thus, we believe that abbreviated or shortened cases are appropriate for this book. They allow us to address a number of issues that we may otherwise have been forced to ignore.

We have separated the cases that we include into several broad categories: organization issues in business ethics, organization issues in clinical ethics, organization issues in professional ethics, and organization issues in research ethics. We preface the introduction of each group of cases with a discussion of the particular perspective to which the case is related. Although the majority of our readers will not be professionally associated with academic research institutions, we have included cases that illustrate the challenges these organizations must meet to support their commitment to research ethics. Although these cases are "specialized," they are excellent examples of the results that can be expected if an organization does not support its stated values in pursuit of its mission. In addition, attention to research ethics issues is becoming more important in many nonacademic HCOs as they become more involved in clinical research studies.

We offer no commentary on these cases and we offer no questions or guidelines to help the reader analyze them. Our concern is to include cases that demonstrate the role of organization ethics activities in the formation and support of a positive ethical climate. Commentary and questions are not necessary. Indeed, we believe that by guiding the discussion we may limit our readers' imaginations. We offer instead a framework of case analysis (appendix B) that can be used by less experienced readers.

In some instances, it has not been easy to decide how to categorize these cases—that is, whether a case represents primarily an organization issue in business ethics, clinical ethics, or professional ethics. One important point of healthcare organization ethics is that a case may represent a number of issues. Consider a case in which a physician, whose compensation is tied to performance-based criteria, which, in turn, is tied to resource utilization, has made a questionable decision about a patient's care; or consider a case in which "administrative" issues result in infringements of confidentiality for an individual or groups of individuals. What criteria should be used in assigning these cases? Issues associated with all three aspects of healthcare ethics may be involved in both cases. For instance, in the first example, certainly we would want to examine any clinical ethics issue that may arise from a questionable decision about patient care, and that examination will almost certainly move us into the realm of professional ethics issues. But we may also decide to investigate the mechanism that could have influenced the questionable decision—the compensation arrangement. Indeed, if we suspect that the compensation arrangement is the cause of the difficulty, we *must* investigate it (or physicians will probably make questionable decisions again); and so we would confront questions of ethics in contractual arrangements. This may take us into the realm of business ethics. Therefore, instead of trying to decide which issue seems to predominate, we have assigned the cases on the basis of where the problem manifests itself. If the physician's decision is questioned at the bedside, we have viewed the case as an organization issue in clinical ethics, regardless of where the source of the problem may be. Alternatively, if the physician's decision is questioned through utilization review, we have viewed the case as an organization issue in business ethics.

Below we present a case that contains within it ethical issues related to an HCO's professional, clinical, and business activities.

High-Quality Health Systems was formed by the merger of the only two hospitals in a medium-sized, midwestern city. Each of the two hospitals had enjoyed a good reputation before the merger, but each had attracted patients who maintained loyalty to their particular institution. The process leading to the merger had been contentious. Because it seemed unlikely that either institution could continue to operate alone in the existing healthcare climate, the merger was approved on purely economic grounds. The decision left many people in the community unhappy. Immediately following the merger, the new system instituted a public relations campaign to inform the citizens of the advantages of the merger and to address a number of specific concerns that citizens had voiced. One of the major concerns, which became a focus of a public relations campaign, was continuity of medical staff, so patients would not be forced to change doctors.

Before the merger, one of the hospitals had entered into a number of exclusive contracts with individual physicians and physicians' groups. These contracts allowed only those physicians with whom the hospital had contracted to practice in the hospital. Other qualified physicians in the community were excluded from practice in the hospital. Exactly how to treat these contracts following the merger had not been worked out beforehand.

Following the merger, the group of anesthesiologists who had had the exclusive contract for anesthesiology services in one hospital demanded a $1 million payoff. They claimed that the exclusive contract had been broken and that this would present a significant financial burden for the group. In conjunction with this demand, the nurse anesthetists who had worked directly for the anesthesiologist group, and who now would be employees of the system, demanded that the system continue to pay them the same salaries that they had received before the merger (the nurse anesthetists at the other hospital were being paid a significantly lower salary).

The CEO of the system was unsure how to proceed. The system's lawyers advised that breaking the exclusive contracts could lead to significant financial liability. The public relations firm advised that disclosing this situation to the public would have an adverse effect on the public relations campaign. The director of human relations told the CEO that the system needed all of the nurse anesthetists, but that increasing their salaries would be a financial drain and would lead to demands for salary increases from other employees at all levels. The CEO scratched his head and paged the newly appointed chair of the organization ethics committee.

In the above case, the HCO's clinical staff, its board of directors and administration, and ultimately its patients and the community have a stake in the outcome of the case. Each group has a legitimate perspective. However, a number of these perspectives are in conflict, and the resolution of these conflicts has the potential to affect patient care adversely. An appropriate resolution of these issues would require attention to resources but, more importantly, it would require attention to the organization's values and mission and the mechanisms by which the values and mission are articulated and maintained. This is appropriate work for an effective organization ethics program.

We do not believe that it is enough to present the kind of challenges healthcare organizations and their stakeholders face daily without addressing how they can respond to these problems. Although organization ethics is in its infancy, some HCOs have recognized and embraced these challenges and are attempting to address them through explicit mechanisms. In appendixes C, D, and E, we present the stories of three HCOs and how they developed and introduced these mechanisms and the challenges they faced in doing so. We have selected these HCOs carefully. They are varied in terms of their of structure and the communities they serve, and each organization has chosen a different path to implement organization ethics activities. But in all three cases, we believe that the formation of organization ethics activities has had a significant and positive effect on stakeholders' relationships with these organizations. We hope that these examples will be of immediate and practical help to others who are beginning to tackle these difficult issues.

This book illustrates some of the specific challenges HCOs face related to organizational ethics. These challenges arise from the decisions that HCO administrators, clinicians, and staff must make on behalf of the organization and its stakeholders—including its most important stakeholder—the patient.

But, as we stated earlier, each stakeholder group has its own perspective. For this reason we have included several codes of ethics as Appendix F, for readers' reference while they work through the cases. It may be obvious why codes of ethics from the American Medical Association, the American Nurses Association, the Council of Medical Specialties Society, and the World Medical Association (the *Declaration of Helsinki*) are included; it may be less obvious why the codes of ethics of the Healthcare Information and Management Systems Society and the American College of Healthcare Executives were included.

HCOs continue to evolve in response to their external environments and to emerging technologies that require the services and talents of a diverse number of stakeholder groups. While we acknowledge the importance of all HCO stakeholder groups, some have emerged as critical to the success of HCOs, and their roles will not diminish in the future. The inclusion of their perspectives is necessary to sustain the ethical climate of organizations.

Healthcare executives and information managers currently have significant roles in HCOs, and these roles will grow as systems evolve and become more technologically complex. For instance, HCOs have become dispensers of information as well as keepers of information, and the ramifications of how this information is treated have important consequences for the strategic direction of HCOs as well as every HCO stakeholder—including patients. Similarly, the role of healthcare executives has advanced, from that of coordinator and manager of the many diverse operations of an HCO, to that of decision maker regarding the kind, quantity, and quality of an HCO's operations. These decisions have strategic implications, and may affect every stakeholder of an HCO—including patients and the communities served. Thus, the perspectives of these groups is important in sustaining the ethical climate of HCOs.

We believe that, if taken seriously, organization ethics will help HCOs reclaim the social and moral power they have lost over the past two decades of frenzied economic activity and allow them to refocus on their ultimate justification—appropriate patient care.

NOTES

1. Joint Commission on Accreditation of Healthcare Organizations, "Patient Rights and Organizational Ethics: Standards for Organizational Ethics," in *1996 Comprehensive Manual for Hospitals* (Oakbrook Terrace, Ill.: Joint Commission on Accreditation of Healthcare Organizations, 1996), 95-97.

2. The Virginia Healthcare Ethics Network is made up of individuals and organizations interested in promoting ethical decision making in all aspects of patient care. In 1999 it had twenty-eight member institutions.

3. The Federal Sentencing Guidelines were initiated in 1984 by the U.S. Congress, which sought to correct what many critics perceived as unevenly applied justice by passing the Sentencing Reform Act of 1984 (Title II of the Comprehensive Crime Control Act of 1984). The Sentencing Reform Act established the U.S. Sentencing Commission, an independent agency in the judicial branch, composed of seven voting and two nonvoting *ex officio* members. The commission's purpose is to establish sentencing policies and practices for the federal criminal justice system that will ensure the ends of justice, by promulgating detailed guidelines that prescribe appropriate sentences for offenders who are convicted of federal crimes. The result of the commission's work is the Federal Sentencing Guidelines.

These guidelines distinguish different levels of criminal activity and specify the appropriate restitution and punishment to be associated with that activity. The sentencing court must elect a sentence from within the guideline range, and it may not depart from a guideline-specified sentence unless a particular case presents atypical features. The court must specify the reasons for any departure from these guidelines. Failure to follow the sentencing guidelines may result in an appeal by either the defendant or the government.

In 1991, an extension of the guidelines applied them to organizations found guilty of violating federal law. The guidelines state that an "organization" means "a person other than an individual." Under this definition, "persons" include corporations, partnerships, associations, joint-stock companies, unions, trusts, pension funds, unincorporated organizations, governments and their political subdivisions, and nonprofit organizations. Healthcare organizations, whether nonprofit or for-profit, incorporated or unincorporated, are included under this definition.

4. U.S. Department of Justice, "Sentencing of Organizations, Federal Sentencing Guidelines." Available at <http://www.ussc.gov/guide/ch8web.htm>.

5. B. Victor and J. Cullen, "The Organizational Bases of Ethical Work Climates," *Administrative Science Quarterly* 33 (1988): 101-25.

6. For more information on the Allegheny debacle, search the World Wide Web for the NewsLibrary Document Delivery and go to the *Philadelphia Inquirer.* Search those archives for articles on the Allegheny Health System. A good starting point is <http://newslibrary.krmediastream.com/eg(document/nl_auth?DBLIST=pi98&DOCUM=23132>.

7. W.T. Lynch, "Teaching Engineering Ethics in the United States," *IEEE Technology & Society Magazine* 15, no. 4 (Winter 1997): 27-36; D.J. Self and E.M. Ellison, "Teaching Engineering Ethics: Assessment of Its Influence on Moral Reasoning Skills," *Journal of Engineering Education* 87, no. 1 (1998): 29-34.

8. J. Kolodner, *Case-Based Reasoning* (San Mateo, Calif.: Morgan Kaufman, 1993); J.L. Kolodner, "Improving Human Decision Making through Case-Based Decision Aiding," *AI Magazine* 12, no. 2 (Summer 1991): 52-8.

9. J. Rest, "Can Ethics be Taught to Adults?" *Taking Sides* 12 (1988): 22-6.

Part One

Organization Issues in Business Ethics

1

Introduction to Organization Issues in Business Ethics

Patricia H. Werhane

THE COMPARTMENTALIZATION OF ISSUES IN HCOs

Until the recent era of managed care, business issues in healthcare organizations (HCOs) were relatively insulated from clinical issues. The hospital at earlier stages of its development operated on a combination of charitable and equitable premises, allowing for the provision of care to be separated from financial support. Physicians, who were primarily responsible for clinical care, constituted an independent power nexus within the hospital and were governed by their own professional codes of ethics. In exchange for a great deal of control over their conditions of practice, they took almost complete responsibility for patient care. Thus, clinical and professional ethics could to some extent be kept apart from business issues. This compartmentalization was aided by the fact that virtually all care was reimbursed from some source or another. In addition, many HCOs were not categorized or treated as businesses, although of course they were presumed to be governed by the same expectation for good management as any other organization.

Today, this separation of powers and of issues is less possible. Still, in analyzing ethical issues for HCOs, we are tempted to separate business issues from clinical or professional issues. Ethical issues in the management of an HCO are often distinguished from issues that arise in clinical practice, and those, in turn, are distinguished from the challenges experienced by the professionals who carry out that practice. But this separation of issues is based on a misperception. In a contemporary HCO, financial, clinical, and professional issues are all so interrelated that one cannot neatly distinguish, say, the cost of a magnetic resonance imaging (MRI) from a patient's need for it, or from the professional expertise that determines the desirability of that protocol. Indeed, distinguishing business issues from issues raised by clinical ethics, or from research issues, or from the responsibilities of healthcare professionals, may be detrimental to an HCO, to patients, and to the long-term professional commitment of healthcare specialists. This is because economic issues play a role in providing healthcare in every setting. Even in the "good old days" before managed care, healthcare professionals had to earn a living, and hospitals and clinics had to survive economically even on charity or governmental support. So setting apart economic issues as if economic sustainability had no role in healthcare is not helpful because economic issues have always affected the quantity, quality, and kind of healthcare that can be provided. The cases in this section illustrate how economic interests intersect with professional and clinical concerns in modern HCOs.

WHY HCOs ARE DIFFERENT FROM OTHER BUSINESS ORGANIZATIONS

Several characteristics of an HCO complicate our understanding of the economic and organizational aspects of healthcare and therefore preclude identifying HCOs with other non-health-related business organizations. These include the following:

1. Mission

Few corporations define their mission solely in terms of profitability. However, whatever the mission, a goal of any for-profit business firm is the economic well-being of its shareholders. In an HCO, there is no such tight relationship between the rationale of the organization's existence and the condition for its economic survival. The difference between garden-variety corporations and any HCO (whether a for-profit organization or not) is that the primary mission of HCOs is always the provision of health services to individuals and populations. This constitutive goal stands in an uneasy relationship with an organization's economic ends. What is strange is not that an HCO is concerned with efficiency, profitability, or—at least—economic survival. The trouble begins when an HCO realigns its mission or creates an organizational culture in which efficiency, productivity, or profitability become the first priorities.

2. Patient Priority

In any organization, how one prioritizes value-creating activities determines the nature of stakeholder relationships. It is true that in many excellent companies profitability is only one of a number of goals such as integrity, customer satisfaction, employee well-being, and respect for community. Nevertheless, no for-profit entity can stay in business very long if it *loses* money. So, while customers may be a set of important stakeholders, they are not the only primary stakeholders. This is not the case in HCOs, where patients—the consumers of the healthcare services provided by HCOs—have a privileged status.

3. Separation of Customer-Payer and Consumer-Patient

In HCOs, recipients of healthcare services are usually not the payers. In HCOs, the correlation between consumer and payer is very different than that which is found in other businesses, and the stakeholder role of "customer" is ambiguous. Various forms of insurance, employer-sponsored health plans, or government agencies purchase health coverage for the individuals and patient groups who are the actual and potential patients for a given HCO. This three-way relationship complicates accountability between the parties affected in healthcare delivery. Unlike the typical consumer, the patient may have no choice to go elsewhere or to change healthcare providers. Even in cases where the recipient of healthcare services is also the payer, the consumer-patient is often ill and vulnerable. So, unlike ordinary consumers, patients cannot be expected always to exercise their choices coherently.

4. Central Role of Professionals

Healthcare professionals—physicians, nurses, and members of other allied health professions—play a key role in the capacity of an HCO to deliver the services central to its definition and mission. It is the healthcare professional, not the manager, who is responsible for delivering care. One cannot gloss over, trade off, or subordinate professional commitments to patient health. Not only would this be morally irresponsible, but it would imperil the mission of any HCO. Typically, healthcare professionals belong to and are accredited by independent professional associations. Many if not all healthcare professionals consider themselves primarily bound by the ethical prescriptions of their profession, preeminent among which are their duties to their patients.

5. Community and Public Health

Despite the ability of HCOs to define and restrict the patient population they serve, community access and public health are always part of the accountability equation, because of the societal expectation that HCOs *should* serve the public's healthcare needs.

6. Healthcare Markets

A number of factors complicate healthcare markets. There is an obvious information asymmetry between managers and healthcare professionals, and between professionals and customers or patients. For this reason, along with the issue of patient vulnerability, an HCO's healthcare customers are never "fully informed" customers. If "buyer beware" was ever an appropriate slogan, it clearly does not apply to HCOs. There is also an information asymmetry among HCOs. Competitive HCOs do not have access to customer (patient) information in ways in which other business enterprises have access to market information. So, ordinary competitive relationships are not possible in the healthcare market. Additionally, there is a asymmetry between supply and demand. HCOs cannot respond to all market demands and, in particular, they cannot respond to the demands of the uninsured. Finally, there is a pricing asymmetry. Some patients or patient groups cannot pay for what they consume, while others pay for more than they consume.

These six distinguishing features, and there are others, give ample evidence that HCOs should be studied apart from other business organizations. Although business ethics provides some tools for that study, one cannot merely conflate HCOs with other business organizations.[1]

STAKEHOLDER THEORY

A tool from business ethics that can help us to analyze the cases in this section and other sections of this book is *stakeholder theory.* Stakeholder theory is an approach to organization ethics that asks decision makers to take into account the rights and interests of the broad range of individuals, professionals, and organizations who interact with, affect, and are affected by organizational decision making. Broadly defined, stakeholders are "groups or individuals who benefit from or are harmed by, and whose rights are violated or respected by, corporate actions."[2] Focusing more narrowly, a stakeholder is any individual or group whose role-relationships with an organization helps to define an organization and its mission, purpose, or goals; "is vital to the survival, and success [or well-being] of the corporation,"[3] and is affected by the organization and its activities. In a modern HCO, the primary or most important stakeholders commonly include patients, professionals, employees, managers, insurers and other payers, owners/shareholders, suppliers, and the community.

Stakeholder theory argues that the goal of any organization is, or should be, the flourishing of the firm and all its primary stakeholders. That purpose is identified with stakeholder interests. Evans and Freeman make the following argument: "The very purpose of a firm [and thus its managers] is to serve as a vehicle for coordinating stakeholder interests. It is through the firm [and its managers] that each stakeholder group makes itself better off through voluntary exchange. The corporation serves at the pleasure of its stakeholders, and none may be used as a means to the ends of another without full rights of participation of that decision. . . . Management bears a fiduciary relationship to its stakeholders and to the corporation as an abstract entity."[4]

Stakeholder obligations are more complex for HCOs than for other business organizations. For example, an HCO has obligations to its employee-professionals (1) because they are moral agents, (2) because they are employees, and (3) because they are professionals and hired *as professionals.* On the other hand, healthcare professionals have role obligations to the HCO that employs them, role obligations to patients, and role obligations to their profession and its associations. They may also have role obligations to the communities they serve and to healthcare payers. In addition, they have ordinary moral obligations to all of these populations by the simple fact of their existence in the community.

How does one evaluate and prioritize various stakeholder claims? Even not-for-profit or charitable HCOs must survive. In the increasingly competitive healthcare climate, economic stability even for the most successful HCOs has become a critical issue. How does one prioritize an HCO's economic sustainability against other claims—in particular, those defined by the mission to provide healthcare services to patients and populations? In fact, there is a simple method for prioritizing the claims of various stakeholders in HCOs. Even though economic concerns are part of almost every HCO today, these organizations have distinguishing characteristics that makes them worth considering apart from other businesses or charitable enterprises. Because the HCO's mission is to provide healthcare services, the primary stakeholders in any HCO are the patients or patient population it serves. Because the primary value-creating activity of an HCO is excellence in patient care, and because survival in the healthcare industry requires the provision of excellent professional services, healthcare professionals are the second most important stakeholders. Third, stakeholders who are concerned with long-term organizational viability that includes financial stability are necessary for the continuation of the HCO and the quality of its services. Finally, because health is considered a public good, the community and the public are part of the stakeholder equation.

In summary, stakeholder theory contributes to our thinking about HCOs and the organizational ethical issues they face in the following ways. First, it helps us to prioritize stakeholders who affect and are affected by the organization (in particular, patients, professionals, managers, and payers) and their value-creating activities in a manner that is consistent with the complex nature of HCOs and that does not dilute the importance of any single stakeholder. Second, stakeholder theory elaborates on reciprocal accountability relationships that have been written about in the medical literature but have not been connected to organizational accountability.[5] Stakeholder theory provides a moral framework for evaluating not only stakeholder relationships but also organizations, their missions, and their value-creating activities. Thus, stakeholder theory provides a framework to think about *organization* ethics for healthcare, while including the dimensions of professional, clinical, and managerial ethics. How one deals with the uniqueness and complexity of an HCO, taking into account all these dimensions, is the subject of the cases that follow.

NOTES

1. P. Werhane, "Business Ethics, Stakeholder Theory and the Ethics of Healthcare Organizations," *Cambridge Quarterly of Healthcare Ethics* 9, no. 3 (1999): 169-81.

2. R.E. Freeman, "Stakeholder Theory and the Modern Corporation," reprinted in *Ethical Issues in Business,* 6th ed., ed. T. Donaldson and P.H. Werhane (Upper Saddle River, N.J.: Prentice Hall, 1999), 247-57, p. 250.

3. Ibid., 250.

4. W. Evan and R.E. Freeman, "A Stakeholder Theory of the Modern Corporation: Kantian Capitalism," in *Ethical Theory and Business,* 4th ed., ed. T. Beauchamp and N. Bowie (Englewood Cliffs, N.J.: Prentice Hall, 1988), 104.

5. E.J. Emanuel and L.L. Emanuel, "What Is Accountability in Health Care?" *Annals of Internal Medicine* 124 (1996): 229-39.

2

A Good Neighbor

Ann E. Mills

A small hospital system is located in Townsville, a wealthy suburban town just south of a large metropolis. The area east and west of Townsville is rural and devoted to farming. Some farmers are prosperous, but many are not. Townsville prides itself on its environmental consciousness. Its board of supervisors, which is elected every two years, works hard to ensure that zoning laws protect the natural beauty of the town.

Townsville Hospital was incorporated thirty years ago as a nonprofit organization and has grown along with the town. Its board of governors has strong ties with both the community and local industry. Because Townsville is a relatively small town, some board members have apparent conflicts of interest. In particular, board member Mr. Barton is also majority owner and chief executive officer (CEO) of Medical Waste, Inc., with which the hospital contracts to handle its medical waste.

Medical Waste, Inc., has been in the disposal business for many years. Mr. Barton's father founded it as a simple waste hauler. Under Mr. Barton's leadership, the company is expanding to provide medical waste collection, transportation, and disposal services for healthcare professionals, nuclear pharmacies, small hospitals, funeral homes, and biotechnical firms. He envisions that Medical Waste will provide "cradle-to-grave" services that make use of cost-effective technology.

Mr. Barton is committed to a clean environment and to the appropriate growth of Townsville. He believes that his company will prosper by taking what he considers to be the right approach to medical waste management. The transition, however, has not been smooth. The company has had to employ new technologies and educate customers about new standards. The transition has been costly, and several times Medical Waste has come perilously close to bankruptcy. Even now, the company faces an uncertain future.

Mr. Barton was appointed to the hospital's board fifteen years ago. Medical Waste, Inc., had just begun its transition from a simple hauler and had secured its first disposal contract with Townsville Hospital. At that time, Mr. Barton expressed his concern about the potential conflict of interest inherent in his position. The board, aware of Mr. Barton's concerns, assured him that disclosure to the board and to the press would be an adequate safeguard against any appearance of "favoritism" in the hospital's contractual relationships. Over the years, Mr. Barton has conscientiously detailed in writing to board members and to the local press any agreement made between his company and the hospital.

Mr. Barton seeks to bring down the cost of hauling medical waste through a variety of techniques, all of which have met EPA (Environmental Protection Agency) approval. The savings that he has generated have helped the hospital open a primary-care clinic in the rural area adjacent to Townsville. The clinic runs a successful outreach program.

The techniques used by Medical Waste, Inc., include the chemical alteration of waste before transportation and the provision of appropriate bins and liners. In addition, Mr. Barton has recommended that the hospital employ in-hospital systems to reduce the cost of transportation and disposal of medical waste. One of these techniques is called a "sharps eater."

A sharps eater system is simple and easy to use by trained staff. It decontaminates sharps (needles, knives) and other related items into safe, nonhazardous waste that may be disposed of by normal procedures. Not only does this technique reduce the cost of waste, but it protects against infection. Used, contaminated sharps are placed in a heavy-duty plastic disposal unit. A hardening agent is dropped into the unit when it is full, and the cover is replaced. The container can then be disposed of through regular trash procedures.

Appropriate staff members have been trained to use the sharps eater system. In spite of all the precautions taken by the hospital and Medical Waste to ensure that hazardous trash is monitored and disposed of properly, a mistake occurred in the pediatrics ward when the usual supervisor was out sick. The unit containing contaminated sharps was not allowed to harden properly. As a result, the disposal unit spilled in the dumpsite that serves Townsville and its adjoining counties. The spillage was found by a maintenance worker, who immediately reported it to the local police.

There was an immediate uproar from the town's media. The media focused on Medical Waste, Inc. as the prime culprit. Reporters detailed the relationship between Mr. Barton and the hospital, implying that the relationship was too "cozy" and that kickbacks might be involved. The Townsville Board of Supervisors was called on to comment on the relationship. The town board reacted cautiously, saying only that an investigation might be warranted.

The board of Townsville Hospital calls a special meeting to decide the hospital's best course of action. The CEO expresses concern that intense public scrutiny could hurt the hospital's revenues and endanger the hospital's relationships with other suppliers. However, he believes that, if Mr. Barton resigns from the board and severs his relationship with the hospital, the contractual arrangement between the hospital and Medical Waste, Inc., can be salvaged.

3

A Local Resource

Jonathan D. Moreno

A newly hired marketing director of a once-pre-eminent medical center in a metropolitan area is discussing the possibility of an alliance with the director of a local television health channel (WCAD-TV).

The metropolis is located in the state's central region. The area north of the city is a popular living area among young professionals and their families. The population of this area has become increasingly affluent as a result of the influx of a large number of "high-tech" businesses that have migrated to the area from California. These demographic changes prompted the two smaller hospitals and their associated clinics that had previously served the area to merge into one larger system—the Northern Area Healthcare System (NAHS). This merger allowed managers to combine their facilities, eliminate duplicate and excess capacity, renovate older structures, increase the array of medical services offered, and increase physicians' salaries in order to retain and enhance professional staff. Many of the medical center's well-known clinicians have moved to NAHS because of its attractive reimbursement rates and "cutting-edge" technologies.

The metropolitan medical center, which, in contrast to NAHS, serves a large number of uninsured patients (including indigent persons and the working poor), views this new hospital system as a serious competitive threat. State and local reimbursement for indigent care has fallen for three consecutive years, and the medical center is losing its insured base, as employers are moving to the more thriving northern area of the state. The medical center hopes that the inroads that managed care is making in the state will work to its favor. However, even though the center's rates have remained competitive with those of NAHS, its image has taken a serious battering over the past few years.

The medical center's top administration has asked all department chairs and directors to consider the competitive threat of NAHS and to suggest ways in which the medical center might meet it. The marketing director has conscientiously explored the potential of one such avenue and has received permission from top administration to pursue it. She spends $200,000 annually to purchase thirteen thirty-second weekly ads. Her research shows that, although NAHS does not seem to have an advertising budget equal to that of the medical center (NAHS airs ads less frequently), its physicians are featured more often during broadcast segments on health topics. For instance, the weekly television show *The Children's Doctor* consistently features pediatricians from NAHS, and this affiliation is referred to throughout the show. Not only does this practice bring NAHS valuable publicity, but it leads viewers to credit NAHS for the information broadcast by the show. The medical center's marketing director believes that these information segments amount to free advertising for NAHS. She asks the director of WCAD-TV for equal time for the medical center in the production of information broadcasts.

The director of the healthcare channel is worried. The medical center is a large account for the station, and he does not want to lose it to his downstate competitor whose shows also reach the local population. He agrees that physicians from NAHS have been featured more often than medical center physicians on *The Children's Doctor,* but he argues that the reason for this is the qualifications and expertise of the physicians associated with NAHS. For instance, 96 percent of all pediatricians associated with NAHS are board certified, and only 20 percent of the medical center's pediatricians are board certified. Further, the show is viewed by a well-informed audience that is interested in obtaining the best information available. This audience is aware that the medical center has suffered from a "brain drain" in the past few years.

The marketing director of the medical center is not impressed. "We have qualified and excellent pediatricians on our staff. We don't need to mention those kinds of statistics in any healthcare segment we do. We are not interested in misrepresenting ourselves, but there is no reason why a show produced with us could not be just as informative as any you produce in cooperation with NAHS. We are, and we want to remain, a local resource for both you and the community."

The marketing director continues, "We insist on being featured more often in your healthcare segments—or else this account goes south. Your cooperation with NAHS in producing these shows is hurting us. We are paying you more in advertising fees, and fair is fair."

4

A Question of Satisfaction

Carrington L. Bailey

A senior management meeting is being held in the conference room that adjoins the office of the chief executive officer (CEO) of Southwest Hospital (SWH), a large hospital that serves the central region of a southwestern state. The hospital has successfully survived the competition generated by managed care because of the excellent and compassionate care it provides to its patients. This excellence is consistently reflected in the hospital's satisfaction surveys, which are used in negotiations with SWH's managed-care customers. But SWH's external business environment is changing. Recently, SWH competitors have formed a system that offers "one-stop shopping." The system, called Quality Care, comprises a large tertiary-care/acute-care facility, two smaller hospitals, outpatient clinics, and several nursing homes. Because the system is vertically integrated, it can offer certain services more conveniently than SWH does. SWH's management team has been able to renegotiate its current managed-care contracts on reasonably favorable terms because its patient satisfaction surveys are much higher than those of Quality Care. However, Quality Care has just released its patient surveys to the local newspaper. These surveys point to a trend of rapidly increasing satisfaction from Quality Care's patients. SWH is concerned that its competitive advantage will be eroded in its negotiations with managed-care organizations for the next fiscal year.

The chief operating officer (COO), Mr. Norton, outlines the situation to the administrators in the crowded room. He explains that he has hired a consulting firm to review SWH's current procedures in the hope of making improvements that will directly and positively affect patient (customer) satisfaction. He introduces the consultant, who is a senior partner in a nationally known public relations firm that specializes in hospital consulting and has ties to healthcare industry think tanks based in Washington, D.C.

The consultant, Ms. Avert, is dressed in a crisp linen suit and is impeccably groomed. She radiates confidence as she addresses the worried-looking senior management team. "SWH has a tremendous reputation. Your satisfaction studies have consistently been high because you combine technical excellence with a real concern for and dedication to the patients who are your customers. But you have to do better to protect your competitive advantage so that you can continue to differentiate yourself from Quality Care."

Ms. Avert continues, "My team has reviewed procedures in traditionally troublesome areas, like admittance and transfer, and we are prepared to offer some suggestions. I am afraid, though, that the improvements we will suggest will involve increased investment in technology and some intensive learning on the part of staff in these areas. These changes will be substantive and permanent, but they will require time to show results. Unfortunately, SWH does not have a lot of time. Contracts are negotiated yearly, and we are already into the fourth month of your fiscal year. Let's talk about what we can do to increase positive survey results."

"I have reviewed your mission and values statements. You state that staff will be concerned, caring, and compassionate with all customers treated by SWH. In your survey of patients, you ask whether or not this concern has been demonstrated. You get good marks, but they could be higher. So let's focus on fulfilling that vision quickly. I suggest a short but intensive training session attended by any staff members who may have contact with patients. Staff, including physicians, will be trained to use certain key words and phrases in their interactions with customers. For instance, all staff will ask, 'Are you comfortable?' at the end of any interaction. Your satisfaction survey asks customers to rank SWH on a scale of one to five on the question, 'Did SWH staff show appropriate concern for your comfort?' You get a three. We could bring it to a five. Another example is to train staff to respond to thanks from customers by saying with an expression of openness, 'I care.' This can be correlated with the question on your survey that asks, 'Do you think that SWH staff demonstrated care and compassion during your stay at SWH?' "

An older man sitting at the back of the room frowns and asks to speak. "Are you sure that implementing such a program is necessary? Is it ethical? Will this program offend our staff who really care about their work?"

Ms. Avert responds brightly, "I see no harm in helping you realize the values SWH has set for itself. There is no harm in teaching staff to demonstrate the values they care about in direct customer care in a way that could make a difference for SWH. Besides, just look at the success Quality Care is having with this program. Do you want to be left behind?"

5

Compassionate but Costly Care

Edward M. Spencer

St. Francis Hospital is revered for its mission, to treat patients who are dying of cancer, and for its compassion in fulfilling this mission. St. Francis has instituted a number of innovative, highly praised interventions that allow these terminally ill patients and their families to receive individualized and caring treatment. Attention is paid to total pain control and to all aspects of care that support the patient's and family members' physical, psychological, and spiritual well-being.

The accommodations at St. Francis have been described as similar to a luxury hotel. The meals are individually prepared by highly trained chefs and can be specially ordered; wine, beer, and mixed drinks are available; and smoking is allowed in certain lounges. Although more costly than other institutions that care for dying patients, St. Francis is the primary referral center for end-of-life care for almost all of the physicians in the community.

The cost for care at St. Francis is about $800 per day, while the cost for other hospice units in other institutions in the community is $150 to $200 per day. Recently, the three largest health-maintenance organizations (HMOs) in the community have informed their enrollees and their providers (including St. Francis) that they will no longer pay more than $200 per day for end-of-life care. St. Francis administrators know that they cannot operate at a loss and that their patients will not be able to pay the difference if the HMO refuses to pay for the care at St. Francis.

A member of the hospital's board of directors is a state legislator who introduces a bill in the state legislature, "The Compassionate Care Act." The bill requires insurance companies and HMOs to pay for treatment in any "hospital which cares exclusively for the dying." The only hospital operating in the state that meets this definition is St. Francis. This bill is strongly supported by the majority party, the American Association of Retired Persons (AARP), church leaders, and community physicians who care for the dying. It is expected to pass and be signed into law by the governor.

The HMOs, other health insurance companies, and a group of physicians concerned about the overall cost of medical care and the use of limited healthcare resources begin a public relations campaign to "inform the public of the irrational use of scarce healthcare resources." This coalition makes public a letter it has sent to the St. Francis board member and legislator, which asks him to withdraw the bill based on St. Francis Hospital's and the Roman Catholic Church's stated and proven commitment to the betterment of the overall health of the community.

6

Giving Back to the Community

Freeman Suber

Dr. Brown, an African-American physician, recently finished her training at a prominent teaching hospital in New York City. She is a board-certified internist. She decides to return to the inner-city neighborhood of her childhood. She wants to work in a community where she knows she is needed. She knows that, regardless of income level, communities with a high percentage of African-American and Hispanic residents are more likely than other communities to have a shortage of physicians.[1] She also knows that minority patient populations are generally very loyal to the minority physicians who serve them.[2]

Dr. Brown submits an application for employment to the hospital that serves her old neighborhood. Within a very short time, she receives an invitation for an initial interview. The hospital is affiliated with several other healthcare facilities that serve communities in different areas of the state. Dr. Brown has good feelings about her initial interview with the physician-administrator who helps manage the system. She knows she that has the qualifications for the position, and she knows how sincere she is in her commitment to her profession. She believes that she articulates this fully at her interview. She is confident that she will be asked back for a second interview and that she will be hired by the system and placed in the hospital of her choice.

Several weeks pass. She has not heard anything about the position. She has received other offers of employment, and time is getting short. She must make a decision about her future. She calls the hospital's physician-administrator to inquire about the position and speaks to his assistant who tells her that the position has been filled. She is curious about the selection criteria and process. She asks to speak to the physician-administrator who interviewed her.

The physician-administrator is cordial and apologizes for not getting back in touch with her sooner. He has received notification to invite Dr. Brown to a second interview, but the position for which she would be interviewing is in a facility in an affluent neighborhood north of New York. He explains that the healthcare system's strategic direction is changing. The system is consolidating and forming alliances with healthcare organizations that are designed to serve a different clientele. The hospital for which Dr. Brown wants to work has an existing patient base that contains some of the sicker patients in the general population, and neither the hospital nor the system that owns it can afford the indigent care that the hospital has provided in its past. He goes on to explain that strategic changes necessarily affect the system's recruiting efforts, which will affect the employment locations of system employees.

Dr. Brown asks, "What is the mission of this hospital? Is it such that your system would prevent me from working with minority groups?" The physician-administrator replies that the mission has been, and remains, as follows: "to offer quality healthcare to all members of the community while showing respect for all individuals associated with the hospital." He goes on to explain that economic conditions often dictate which strategies are used to fulfill this mission.

NOTES

1. H. Brody and F.G. Miller, "The Internal Morality of Medicine: Explication and Application to Managed Care," *Journal of Medicine and Philosophy* 23 (1998): 4.

2. R. Lavizzo-Mourey, "The Perceptions of African-American Physicians Concerning Their Treatment by Managed Care Organizations," *Journal of the National Medical Association* 88 (1996): 210-4.

7

Help Wanted

Margaret L. Skelley

The medical center of a large state university enjoys an excellent relationship with the surrounding community. The medical center has always demonstrated concern for the well-being of the community. "Good citizenship" and "active work to serve community needs" are pledges made in the medical center's mission statement, which was formulated more than a century ago.

Operating margins have been healthy in the past, but reimbursement from third-party payers combined with competition from managed care has eroded these margins. Strategies to increase revenues and reduce costs are quietly being discussed by the university's executive vice president, the medical center's chief operating officer (COO), and their respective staffs. These discussions center on identifying means by which expenditures for indigent care can be reduced without sacrificing the medical center's reputation or its relationship with the surrounding urban community. This will be a formidable task.

The executive vice president reports to the president of the university. The COO of the medical center reports to the executive vice president. Together, they are responsible for developing the medical center's strategy as well as formulating and controlling the medical center's budget and operations.

The executive vice president urges the president of the university to secure a vice president for community relations. He argues that the university needs such a position so that it can identify and respond to community concerns. The executive vice president is anxious about the coming budget cuts and their effect on the community. He is concerned that the new policies that the medical center may have to endorse will be misrepresented to the community. He believes that the nonprofit status of the university warrants such a position.

The president of the university agrees. The executive vice president delegates much of the responsibility for the search to the medical center's COO. He indicates that, although the vice president for community relations will technically report to the executive vice president, the COO will be responsible for supporting the new position's salary, supervising the individual on a day-to-day basis, and preparing the individual's annual performance appraisal for the executive vice president's signature.

The chief of medical staff receives a memo detailing the duties and the reporting structure of the new position. She asks her assistant to arrange a meeting with the president of the university. She believes that creating this new position is important both to the medical center and to the community. However, she is concerned that the reporting structure of the new position will create a potential conflict of interest between the COO and the vice president for community relations; even worse, it will create the appearance of a conflict of interest. The chief of medical staff argues that for the new position to be effective the community must be able to trust the person occupying the position to communicate, without bias, the concerns and worries of the community to the leadership of the medical center—that one important role of this position is community advocate. How can the community trust the new vice president for community relations if that person reports to and is evaluated by those responsible for initiating future budget cuts—especially in the area of indigent care? She states that the new position should report to the chief of medical staff, who is in a far better position to understand the needs of the community than the COO.

The president is sympathetic but hesitant. "A similar conflict of interest is apparent in the structure you propose. The COO and, through him, the executive vice president will feel that the new VP's allegiance to you and your staff will compromise any reasonable representation he or she makes on behalf of the community. Your proposal does nothing except move the site of the conflict."

The chief of medical staff has a ready answer, "But our staff operates within a professional code. We are in the best position to judge what is necessary for the community and what is not."

8

Hospital Planning Scenario

Robert D. Wells

For the fiscal year 2000-2001, Valley Children's Health System has four competing new programs that are each requesting funding. The financial services office has indicated that, based on current revenues, only one of the four projects can be funded. As part of the decision-making strategy, the institutional ethics committee has been asked to review these four projects and assess the ethical value of each project as it relates to the hospital's mission.

HOSPITAL MISSION STATEMENT

The mission of Valley Children's Health System (VCHS) is to provide high-quality, comprehensive healthcare to the children of Central California, regardless of their means of payment for services. VCHS serves as the hub of a network of hospitals and physicians, including some that are tied through partnerships and joint ventures in clinical programs and others that are affiliated through shared services and educational ventures. VCHS is a leader in pediatric education and has a residency program that serves as a model in pediatric primary care. It is widely recognized for its culture and values:

Quality:	A commitment to excellence in everything we do; integrity; wholeness.
Service:	Responsiveness to the needs of patients, their families, visitors, and one another.
Caring:	Respect, trust, honesty, and compassion for patients, their families, and one another.
Innovation:	New ideas and practices and constant improvement.

Fun: Humor, joy, and hope permeating our relationships,
                          our work, and our environment.
Resourcefulness: "Can do" attitude, adaptability, tenacity, and stew-
                          ardship.

PROGRAM 1:
EXTRACORPOREAL MEMBRANE OXYGENATION

Extracorporeal membrane oxygenation (ECMO) is a state-of-the-art technology for supporting patients with cardiac problems who cannot be adequately managed on a ventilator. At VCHS, eight to ten patients a year could be placed on ECMO after cardiac surgery or during their care in the neonatal intensive care unit (NICU), rather than dying or being transferred out to another facility. Approximately 40 to 50 percent of patients who receive ECMO survive. The cardiac surgeons, pediatric intensivists, and respiratory technicians are strongly in favor of developing ECMO capability at VCHS. If ECMO were available, VCHS might be able to offer more aggressive cardiac surgical care, rather than having families and patients travel to the University of California at San Francisco (UCSF) or Stanford University for heart transplant and other complex surgical treatments. By removing the patients currently sent out of VCHS, other centers may have difficulty maintaining their programs. The program would cost approximately $1 million to develop and operate per year. Given current reimbursement arrangements, VCHS might recover approximately 50 percent of the cost.

PROGRAM 2:
WESTSIDE PEDIATRIC CLINIC

Children living in the Westside catchment area of Fresno receive relatively poor primary healthcare. There are very few practicing pediatricians in the area, and the vast majority of the population is comprised of impoverished African-American families. VCHS wants to place a clinic in the Westside area and staff it so that a team of pediatricians and allied health providers could see fifty patients per day (10,000 patients per year). Well child care, nutrition, counseling, health education, and other vital services would be provided on site. Although no other programs currently plan to increase medical care access to this underserved population, some healthcare providers believe that VCHS should not compete by providing primary pediatric care. This program would cost approximately $1 million to develop and operate per year. Given current reimbursement arrangements, VCHS might recover approximately 50 percent of the cost.

PROGRAM 3:
KIDNEY TRANSPLANT SERVICE

VCHS has one pediatric nephrologist and is recruiting a second. All candidates who have been interviewed insist that they would only be interested in coming to VCHS if a kidney transplant service were available on site. Currently, all patients who are eligible for transplant are sent to UCSF or Stanford. VCHS has approximately eight to ten patients per year who require transplantation, which is the minimum number needed for a center to maintain a transplant program. By removing the patients VCHS currently sends out, other centers may have difficulty maintaining their programs. In contrast, in order to build a state-of-the-art pediatric nephrology program, VCHS should develop kidney transplant capability. Kidney transplantation is successful for 80 to 90 percent of patients. This program would cost approximately $1 million to develop and operate per year. Given current reimbursement arrangements, VCHS might recover approximately 50 percent of the cost.

PROGRAM 4:
RURAL PEDIATRIC HEALTHCARE SERVICES

Rural District Hospital in the south valley has expressed an interest in developing a joint program to improve the pediatric inpatient and outpatient care for children in the relatively rural area. They have proposed that VCHS develop a pediatric clinic and a ten-bed inpatient unit for small infants and newborns. VCHS would supply two pediatricians and allied staff to offer services to a catchment area that is very rural, tending to serve migrant farm worker families. It is proposed that the clinic will serve fifty patients per day (10,000 patients per year) to allow less critically ill children and infants to remain in their local hospital, rather than traveling forty-five minutes to Fresno. Although no other programs currently plan to increase medical care access to this underserved population, some healthcare providers believe that VCHS should not compete by providing primary pediatric care. This program would cost approximately $1 million to develop and operate per year. Given current reimbursement arrangements, VCHS might recover approximately 70 percent of the cost.

9

Laser Lights

Sue McCoy

A few years ago, Gardenia Hospital accelerated efforts to entice a larger share of the market away from the two hospitals in neighboring towns by opening its new Laser Surgery Center. The grand opening was celebrated with a laser light extravaganza on the Fourth of July, and giant billboards sprang up in the area extolling "the gentle surgery." Ads on the local television station implied that no one would want surgery done any other way.

The new center had cost Gardenia Hospital an astounding amount of money, and maintenance costs were also high. To recoup these costs, the operating room has found innovative ways to charge patients. One charge that particularly galls Dr. Jones, a general surgeon who is a member of the hospital's physician hospital organization (PHO), is the high fee each patient is charged for the presence of the laser instrumentation in the operating room—whether it is used or not.

Dr. Jones has a loyal following of patients and a large referral base. All of his patients and colleagues find him to be a very competent, caring, personable, and conscientious surgeon. In fact, his friends often come to him for informal explanations of their own or family members' medical problems when they have difficulty understanding other doctors.

When Mrs. Hardy asks Dr. Jones to use laser surgery to remove her gallbladder, he carefully explains that laser surgery is a great new technology and—like all new technologies—it has its own special place in the surgeon's armamentarium. There are some procedures, like removal of large red birthmarks on the face, that no other technique will do as well. "But when I am operating inside of your abdomen, you will not be able to tell how I cut, be it with a scalpel, a clip applier, a cautery, or a laser. Furthermore, using the laser is quite expensive and, even though you have good insurance, we doctors need to be as cost-conscious as we can and do our best to avoid unnecessary tests and procedures. If everyone who has surgery wants the laser used just because it's the newest way, your insurance will soon become more expensive."

Today Mr. Neddrick, the PHO administer at Gardenia Hospital, asks Dr. Jones why he does not plan to use the laser when he operates on his sister-in-law, Mrs. Hardy. "Frankly," he says, "you don't use laser surgery nearly as often as the other surgeons. Since you are one of our busiest surgeons, we need the added income from your patients to help pay for the new center."

10

Nurse Staffing Ratios

Judith Andre

City Medical Center (CMC) has changed the way it structures nursing care. Many of the less-skilled activities that were once done by licensed nurses (registered nurses and licensed practical nurses) are now done by unlicensed personnel such as housekeepers and other hospital employees. After brief training, these new workers are being asked to change catheter bags and record urine output, take patients' vital signs, feed patients who cannot feed themselves, give baths, and so on. Part of the incentive for this restructuring is financial. Like most hospitals, CMC is suffering serious financial pressures, and nursing salaries are one of the system's biggest expenses. But it is also hoped that the restructuring will add meaning to the jobs of the "unskilled" hospital employees, who were once told, "Keep still. Don't talk to any patient or family. Just get the room clean." And it is hoped that patient care will be more personal, since patients will see fewer people each day and will be able to ask anyone in the room for the mundane things they need (such as, a glass of water or having the bed cranked up).

The nurse-patient ratio is not much different than it was ten years ago, but, on average, the patients are much sicker (because they leave the hospital at an earlier stage in their recovery). In the units that are restructured, the nurses are convinced that patient care is suffering badly. They believe that the unlicensed personnel do not know what to look for. For example, unlicensed staff do not know what can be learned from listening to blood pressure rather than taking it mechanically; cannot recognize the early signs that decubitus ulcers are setting in; and are unable to recognize the subtle color changes in urine that suggest a bladder infection. As one nurse pointed out, "Even bathing a patient is a holistic, technically skilled job. When I do it, I'm looking for signs of skin breakdown, assessing pain status, mobility, and mental state; educating the patient; and giving him emotional support. Most of this, unlicensed personnel can't do. And I can't do it in the new system because I have so many very sick patients. I can only attend to their most urgent, and most physical, needs. It's impossible now to sit and talk with patients, no matter how frightened, depressed, or lonely they are. We are certainly not living up to our implied promise to give the best care to each patient."

At the CMC nursing staff meeting the following day, this nurse voiced her concerns. The director of patient services, who had just attended a senior management meeting, was sympathetic but told the entire nursing staff that financial survival of the institution was the "bottom-line" issue at the present and that no increase in the nursing staff budget was possible. The director of patient services also called attention to the mission statement of the hospital, which set forth "optimum care for each individual" as the goal. She told the nursing staff that she believed this goal was being accomplished.

11

To Report or Not

Margaret L. Skelley

Dr. B is the epidemiologist and director of infection control for a state-affiliated academic health center in the Midwest. The reportable disease statutes and regulations in Dr. B's state specify that hospitals and other healthcare facilities throughout the state are required to track nosocomial infections (infections not present in patients prior to their admittance to the hospital) and to "rapidly report outbreaks" to the local health department. What constitutes an "outbreak" is not specifically defined in the statute or in the regulations. This determination is left to the discretion of each facility's epidemiologist.

As the hospital's epidemiologist, Dr. B is charged with collecting data on all reportable diseases. He is responsible for determining when the threshold for an outbreak has been met. His staff provides him with data indicating that the rate of several nosocomial infections has been increasing steadily. The increases have been sustained over a period of three and a half months and are statistically significant. Although Dr. B's data lag behind by approximately one month due to data collection limitations, all indications are that the rates will remain at their current elevated levels or may even escalate. In Dr. B's opinion, these increases constitute a nosocomial outbreak and should be reported to the local health authorities.

The hospital is still reeling from the political fallout resulting from intense media attention on a young patient with epilepsy who was left unattended and who suffered a serious fall during a grand mal seizure. The patient, a minor, is now in a persistent vegetative state. The hospital administration, risk management, and the legal counsel for the medical center and the university are highly sensitive about the incident and are searching for any possible angle to lessen the hospital's apparent liability for this extremely unfortunate incident. The situation has enraged the governor as well, who has expressed his concern about its reflection on him and his chances for a Senate candidacy. He is said to have told those close to him that he will "make heads roll" in order to appear to have dealt adequately with the situation.

Dr. B's infection control staff believes that they have identified the probable cause of the outbreak. They have found that healthcare providers are frequently not adhering to basic hand-washing regimens that are required by standard infection control procedures. Observers on the units report that only 30 percent of healthcare workers wash their hands between patient contacts. The situation is even worse in the intensive care units (ICUs), where only 10 percent of physicians wash their hands between patient contacts. The welfare of every patient on every unit of the hospital is jeopardized by this situation. Dr. B plans an aggressive internal communications campaign to increase awareness of the current low levels of hand washing and to emphasize the importance of infection control in the care of patients.

Dr. B relays his findings to the hospital leader and maps out his plans for an aggressive communications campaign. He receives a less than lukewarm response. He is questioned about the state reporting requirements. He is told that, since the parameters defining "outbreak" are not specifically defined, it is highly doubtful that the institution is experiencing an outbreak. Hospital administrators agree that the situation must be monitored closely. However, they instruct Dr. B not to report the nosocomial outbreak to the local health agency. In addition, they advise him not to disseminate data on the levels of hand washing observed on the units and instruct him to limit his campaign to a general message emphasizing the importance of hand washing in any successful infection control effort. He is told to monitor the situation closely.

12

Treatment of Employees during Downsizing

Brian O'Toole

A significant downsizing of almost 10 percent of all employees is planned for XYZ hospital system. The mission leader of XYZ hospital system insists that every effort be made to respect and promote the dignity of employees throughout the entire downsizing process. The mission leader believes that keeping this promise will involve developing criteria for a new policy and procedure that is more in keeping with the hospital's "mission and values" for determining which employees will be "downsized." The senior management team responsible for the downsizing reiterates the organization's long-standing commitment to fairness in its relationships with its employees and agrees to develop a policy and procedure for downsizing that reflects this commitment.

The mission leader identifies a number of possible criteria for inclusion in the new policy. They include the following:

- The skill level of each employee
- The formal education, credentialing, and experience of each employee
- The performance evaluations of and disciplinary actions against each employee
- The seniority of each employee
- The current salary of each employee
- The perceived ability of each employee to learn new skills and roles
- The perceived ability of each employee to work as a team
- The way each employee is judged to embody the mission and values of the organization
- The determination of the extent that each employee needs the position because of personal financial concerns.

The mission leader submits these criteria for inclusion in the downsizing policy, but senior management is uncertain how to weigh each criterion in arriving at a standardized formula for determining which employees will be affected by the downsizing. The organization ethics committee is asked to help determine what weight each criterion should receive.

13

What Kind of Furnace?

Edward M. Spencer

Lonesome Hollow Hospital (LHH) was founded in 1904 in Coalville, a town in the coalfields of southern West Virginia. Since that time, both the hospital and Coalville have grown and prospered. LHH is now a modern medical facility with up-to-date medical equipment and a well-trained and highly regarded staff. LHH is known throughout the area as the best-equipped, best-staffed medical facility for the diagnosis and treatment of diseases related to coal mining. The board of directors and administration at LHH are particularly proud of the strong relationship the hospital has with coal mine operators, the miners' union, and individual miners. They also have a strong community orientation and consider the needs of the community in all of their major decisions. Until now, this has been a mutually satisfying relationship.

Recently it became obvious that LHH needed to modernize its heating system. The present system, which consists of three coal-fired boilers and a steam distribution system of pipes throughout the hospital, was installed in 1947 and no longer meets state and federal environmental standards. A heating consultant hired by LHH recommended that the old system be scrapped and that a modern, efficient gas-electric heating system be installed. When asked whether there was some way coal could be used as the primary fuel for the new system, the heating contractor replied that a coal-fired system would not be nearly as efficient or as easy to control and that, with more stringent environmental standards likely, a coal-fired system would soon become obsolete and have to be replaced again. With this information, the board and senior administration decided to install the recommended gas-electric system.

In keeping with their tradition of openness with the community, the LHH administration announced its decision concerning the replacement of the hospital heating system, and this announcement was carried by the local newspaper and television station. A small but vocal group of environmentalists in the community immediately applauded the hospital's "far-sighted decision" and its "continuing attention to the needs of the community demonstrated by its obvious environmental consciousness."

Unfortunately, the replacement of the hospital's heating system comes at a time when several local coal mines have been forced to close due to a declining market for their coal. LHH's announcement causes much consternation among the coal operators, the union, and the miners. A committee representing these coal interests is formed and meets with the hospital board and administration. At this meeting, the coal interest committee asks the board to reconsider its decision because of the adverse influence the switch to a different fuel would have on other businesses and small industries in the area. The coal interest group argues that many others would follow the hospital's lead, which would cause further damage to the already depressed market for coal in the area. They also argue that there has been a long-standing commitment to mutual support between the coal industry and LHH, and that the commitment from the coal industry to use LHH has allowed the hospital to become the premier institution it is. They note that one of LHH's stated values is "a strong commitment to the study and treatment of the diseases associated with coal mining" and they argue that not supporting the local coal industry is tantamount to abandoning this commitment.

Part Two

Organization Issues in Clinical Ethics

14

Introduction to Organization Issues in Clinical Ethics

Mary V. Rorty

TRADITIONAL CLINICAL ETHICS: A CASE-CENTERED APPROACH

Clinical ethics began because of a perceived need to pay closer attention to ethical issues arising at the bedside and, in particular, to ensure that the rights of the patient are a primary determinant of the direction of medical care.[1] To this end, clinical ethics has relied on a major traditional tenet of professional medical ethics for its primary guidance—that is, it has put care of the individual patient as the first priority in clinical practice. Contemporary clinical ethics has focused almost exclusively on the individual patient and his or her personal autonomy and health, not on the larger community. Although the clinical ethics literature touches upon problems that arise in private practice, the main focus has been on problems that arise in institutional settings, acknowledging the primacy of the healthcare organization (HCO) as the institutional base for clinical ethics. This focus is reflected in this section, which examines clinical ethics cases in its institutional and social context.

Many readers will be familiar with the role of clinical ethics within the HCO. In 1992 the Joint Commission on Accreditation of Healthcare Organizations (JCAHO) mandated that each HCO it accredits have a "mechanism" in place to address ethical issues as they arise in the care of patients.[2] The development of this mechanism was left to individual HCOs, which responded to the JCAHO mandate in various ways, which ranged from one person dominating any activity associated with clinical ethics, to large institutional ethics committees (IECs) with formalized reporting structures and a daunting menu of services. Various alternatives continue to be debated among professionals and academics interested in clinical ethics, but the JCAHO requirement meant that the role of clinical ethics, with its focus on the individual patient as the first priority in clinical practice within the HCO, was ensured.

IECs generally focus on three areas to ensure that the rights of patients are understood and respected within the HCO: education, policy review, and ethics case consultation. The education function of ethics committees, while often including recommendations about community education in ethical issues of concern to HCOs, usually is concentrated on internal education, such as workshops, presentations, and discussions for clinicians who operate in particular clinical areas. Thus, critical care units may focus on end-of-life treatments, neonatal units on pre-viable infants or developmental impairments, and obstetrical units on maternal-fetal conflicts. Information about new policies, recent court cases, or recent local cases that have created or called attention to ethical dilemmas may be discussed in in-service, training, unit or grand rounds, or public forums. Some hospital ethics committees have established libraries or files on publications about experienced or anticipated patient care issues and may make the materials available to practitioners. Education is often correlated with other ethics committee functions, including policy development, and an ethics committee may act as a resource to the larger institution on general ethical issues surrounding patient care such as confidentiality, competence determination, consent and refusal of treatment, and end-of-life care.

The impact of hospital policies upon patient care is so obvious as to need little articulation. Some HCO policies serve as a bridge between federal or state regulations and standards of practice within the institution. The JCAHO requires policy statements and guidelines for many issues associated with patient care, and it is these policies that have been until now the main area of concern for ethics committees.[3] Because clinical ethics committees have traditionally been comprised primarily of clinicians, their review of policies allows for clinical as well as ethical input into policy creation.

Ethics consultation is a service provided by an individual or group to help patients, families, surrogates, healthcare providers, and other involved parties address uncertainty or conflict regarding value-laden issues that emerge in healthcare. Ethics consultation is addressed by one of several mechanisms—the hospital ethics committee, a subset of that committee designated as ethics consultants, or an outside consultant. Frequently the role of the consultation is not to decide ethical issues, but to explore and offer advice about ethically acceptable options, relevant legal cases, or social consensus. Lawyers may offer ethics consultation in some hospitals, and decisions about the clinically appropriate course are often tempered by consideration of what the courts and local jurisdictions consider legal.

Facilitating communication and dispute resolution is a central concern of ethics consultation. The time pressures of care in a busy hospital setting can lead to failures of communication that can produce problems. If patients or family members do not adequately understand the reasons behind decisions about care, or if different members of the care team fail to communicate adequately with one another, misunderstandings and differences of opinion can loom disproportionately large. Although clinical ethics works to "level the playing field" by acknowledging that other clinicians, patients, and families have valid moral positions that must be recognized, nonetheless, its claims are often implicitly addressed to the physician-decision maker.

THE NEED TO EXPAND
THE SCOPE OF CLINICAL ETHICS:
AN ORGANIZATIONAL APPROACH

During the past two decades, at the same time that IECs were being established within institutional settings, the U.S. healthcare system has been undergoing radical changes. One of the more profound changes has been the shift in focus from caring for the individual patient to managing the health of population groups. This shift has meant that new organizational structures were needed to manage the care of populations within the context of a predictable and limited budget.

To manage population groups in the context of relatively inflexible budgets, administrators within HCOs had to develop (or borrow) business techniques that allowed them enough control to achieve their objectives. It became increasingly obvious to clinical staff, administrative staff, patients, and the larger society that administrative policy, rather than individual professionals, directed many clinical decisions in HCOs. As the typical model for healthcare delivery changed from fee-for-service care to some variety of managed care, clinicians found that they had to make accommodations for organizational strictures regarding, for example, the range of available drugs and treatments, billing practices, access to healthcare, financial incentives to reduce utilization of resources, and restrictions on access to specialists and full disclosure to patients. If physicians' decisions are affected by organizational constraints, the goal of clinical ethics—patient protection and advocacy—must allow for this wider area of concern.

The interface between clinical ethics and organization ethics is important and complex. First, many clinical ethics problems have organizational implications. For example, patient privacy and confidentiality of medical information are not simply questions involving the identification of patient charts, but issues that need to be addressed on an organizational level. What safeguards does the hospital medical information system have against unauthorized access to patient information? What protections of patient anonymity does the system require of those who have authorized access? What happens to information gathered for administrative, epidemiological, or research purposes? Are lists of end users of various pharmaceuticals made available to commercial enterprises that may then sell that information? Disclosure is an institutional as well as a physician-patient issue. What rules or conventions does the hospital follow when financial issues are discussed with patients? What rules govern institutional disclosure of policies, proprietary information, or practitioner statistics to patients? To other institutions? To the community? What conflicts of interest or of obligation are created for healthcare professionals who serve an institution in various administrative positions? An accessible forum to discuss such issues is as important for organizational ethics as it is for patient-focused ethics. In the course of resolving a typical clinical ethics case, structural problems are often identified—such as staffing issues, problems with the approved formulary, or the absence of a policy to provide guidance to clinicians. Excellent clinical ethics practice will note those problems and direct them to the appropriate organizational components.

Second, clinical ethics problems often have an organizational analogue. Confidentiality, disclosure, truth-telling, informed consent, and conflicts of interest are as important in organizations as they are in clinical encounters, but an organization's response to the challenge cannot be limited or reduced solely to its clinical responsibility. Insofar as organizations are ethical agents and instruments for healthcare in society, they are subject to the same kinds of ethical expectations that society has of individual healthcare providers. Finally, some clinical ethics problems have organizational causes, such as a change in policy without consideration of the clinical implications; a shift in organizational priorities or values without adequate information, education, discussion, or negotiation with all affected individuals; or inadequate communication among various stakeholders in the institution.

The practice of clinical ethics is an important organizational obligation and an important expectation of society and of various stakeholders within an HCO. It must be protected by the organization. Clinical ethics shares with professional ethics a value that is essential to the HCO as an organization—the primacy of patient care. However, clinical ethics cannot be effective unless it is practiced within the context of the organization. The practice of clinical ethics must be part of organization ethics practice, but not identical to it, and IECs must be integrated into an organization's ethical climate and be able to act comfortably in this context.

THE FUNCTION OF ORGANIZATION
ETHICS WITHIN HCOs

The function of organization ethics, as we conceive of it, is to develop and maintain a consistent ethical climate within an organization. Like clinical ethics, organization ethics is not simply an application of theories from philosophical, business, or biomedical ethics. Instead, it is a practice-focused set of procedures and mechanisms to address ethical problems that arise in organizations that deliver healthcare. Many of those problems are not questions about how to understand or apply clinical or professional ethical obligations; instead, problems arise when clinical, professional, or business ethical obligations conflict with one another. Some issues that are appropriate for organization ethics to address—financial policies, contracts, marketing, financial viability, personnel issues, public relations—are not ordinarily currently addressed by clinical ethics committees. Indeed, many of these issues cannot be appropriately addressed by the usual range of members of clinical ethics committees. Moreover, many of the issues that are most important for clinical ethics and organization ethics are not explicitly addressed by any of the components of the organization. Those include the hierarchical structure of HCOs, power relations within HCOs, and the ethical implications of organizational routines and structures.

Clinical ethics can no longer be limited to the case-centered interpersonal or interprofessional issues that have constituted its major focus in the past. The changing healthcare environment—including the blurring of lines of authority, the alteration of traditional roles, and the increasing impact of organizational issues on patient care—requires a new approach to the overall ethical climate within the HCO. What is needed is a larger, more global vision of the elements of organizational life that affect patient care and an attention to the overall ethical climate of an HCO. Clinical ethics is an important function of HCOs; however, it must be reconceptualized as one of several crucial ethical perspectives, and fostered, integrated, and protected within this larger organizational enterprise.

The cases we have chosen to include as "organization issues in clinical ethics" all represent conflicts that occur at the bedside. However, each case involves issues that might be resolved by focusing on organizational ethics. Although the resolution of these cases may not be the resolution desired by all the parties involved—this seldom happens in a world bound by scare resources—each case can potentially be resolved in a manner that reflects an HCO's stated values while the rights (and obligations) of patients, family members, and patient surrogates are supported.

NOTES

1. J.C. Fletcher et al., ed., *Introduction to Clinical Ethics,* 2nd ed. (Hagerstown, Md.: University Publishing Group, 1997).

2. Joint Commission on Accreditation of Healthcare Organizations, "Patient Rights," in *1992 Accreditation Manual for Hospitals* (Oakbrook Terrace, Ill.: Joint Commission on Accreditation of Healthcare Organizations, 1992): 103-5.

3. Among the issues on which the JCAHO requires policy are informed consent, use of surrogate decision makers, decisions regarding research or clinical trials, refusal of medically indicated treatment, advance directives, pain management, confidentiality of information and security of patient property, complaint resolution, organ procurement and donation, and access to medical records. For an excellent discussion of the functions of ethics committees in HCOs, see J.C. Fletcher and E.M. Spencer, "Ethics Services in Healthcare Organizations," in *Introduction to Clinical Ethics,* 2nd ed., ed. J.C. Fletcher et al. (Hagerstown, Md.: University Publishing Group, 1997), 257-85.

15

Advertising Special Services

Judith Andre and Linda J. Keilman

The hospital has placed billboards throughout the region with the following statement: "Are You a Victim of Sexual or Domestic Assault? Come to Warman Center Where We Treat You Immediately. Our Staff of Counselors and Providers Have Received Special Sensitivity Training in This Area. *You* Are Our Main Concern."

A twenty-five-year-old college student presents to the Warman Center's emergency department stating, "My boyfriend assaulted and raped me and I need help." The registration clerk notices that there are fresh bruises and bleeding on her face, neck, and arms. The student fills out registration information and is asked to sit in the waiting room.

Several hours pass. The young woman approaches the registration clerk and states, "I am really scared. I have pain. I am terribly upset about what has happened to me, and I just can't sit here any longer."

The registration clerk responds, "Haven't you seen all the ambulances come in? We have patients with critical injuries like pneumothorax here. You will have to wait your turn."

Three and a half hours later, when a nurse calls out the student's name to come back, she is no longer in the waiting room.

16

An Impediment

Christy A. Rentmeester

Jo was diagnosed with cancer five years ago. Upon diagnosis, twenty-four-year-old Jo established a relationship with oncologist, Dr. A. Under Dr. A's care, Jo pursued several courses of treatment, including chemotherapy and radiation therapy. These therapies were successful in the short-run. Jo felt well and "cancer free" for two years. She enjoyed time with family and friends, completed graduate school, and spent four months in Korea teaching English. However, a recent checkup revealed that a cancerous mass is growing on Jo's spine, at the neck.

After extensive discussion of her options with Dr. A, Jo decided to undergo surgery to have the cancerous mass removed. Dr. A referred Jo to Dr. M—a surgeon with, in the words of Dr. A, "an uncompromisingly poor bedside manner but the best hands of any neurosurgeon I know."

Jo met briefly with Dr. M later that week. She was given several pamphlets about the type of surgery she would undergo, and she was warned about the risks involved. Her surgery was scheduled. Meanwhile, Jo's illness worsened. Her family was involved in her care along with two nurses who provided her with palliative care and hospice services.

Three days before surgery, Dr. A and the nurses recommended that Jo consider completing an advance directive. Dr. A apologized to Jo for bringing up the prospect of death so abruptly. He expressed concern that Jo's condition was deteriorating more rapidly than he expected and emphasized that Jo should have the opportunity to put her wishes about end-of-life care in writing in the event that her surgery was not successful. Jo agreed and was grateful for the chance to "get some thoughts together." She told Dr. A, "Things may not go well. If they don't, I don't want to be kept alive as a vegetable or comatose or something. I don't want my family to have to deal with my existence that way. I'd rather die than have to be kept alive by machines and tubes."

Jo, her family, Dr. A, and the two nurses involved in Jo's care discussed Jo's wishes and the various components of her advance directive. Her family and caregivers clearly understood and accepted that if Jo had little chance for recovering an acceptable quality of life after the surgery, she wanted to be allowed to die as comfortably as possible. Jo assigned power of attorney for healthcare to her father. The document was signed, witnessed, and implemented according to state law and according to the guidelines set forth in the hospital's information packet. Her father noted that the information packet contained a statement that "all advance directives will be honored to the extent allowed by current law" and that "appropriate surrogate decision makers will have the same authority to make decisions for the patient as the patient would have if she were a capable decision maker."

The day of surgery arrived. Jo was anesthetized, and Dr. M operated for seven hours. The mass was removed, and Jo was moved to the recovery room. For unknown reasons, Jo began to hemorrhage. Despite the best efforts of Dr. M and other clinicians, it appeared unlikely that Jo would recover without significantly compromised neocortical function (that is, she would remain comatose or in a persistent vegetative state).

Jo was observed and treated in the intensive care unit over the next five days. Her condition did not improve. Her family asked Dr. M daily about her prognosis. His position continued to be, "It sometimes takes several weeks to know what the ultimate prognosis will be, so we'll have to wait and see what happens. We're doing all we can."

Jo's family, aware of her wishes, became increasingly unhappy with her continued treatment. They finally confronted Dr. M in the hallway late one night as he hurried down the hall. They mentioned that Jo had an advance directive. Jo's father stated, "This isn't what Jo wants. Jo doesn't want to be hooked up to tubes and machines." Dr. M interrupted, "Are you asking me to turn off Jo's ventilator and stop her drips? If I do this, Jo will die. I will not kill my patient. That's all there is to it. Jo is not in pain, she is not presently terminally ill or in a persistent vegetative state, and she still may recover some function." When asked if he held any hope for Jo to recover sufficiently to be fully aware of her surroundings, Dr. M replied, "I doubt it, but that isn't the point at the moment." When reminded of the hospital's policy concerning advance directives and surrogate decision making, he stated, "That's very well and good for terminal patients, but it doesn't apply to Jo. Another part of the hospital's mission is to treat our patients to the best of our ability so that the patient receives maximum benefit from her hospital stay. If we stop treating her now, we would not be adhering to this mission." He left abruptly following this statement.

Jo's family members were upset. They talked with Dr. A and with Jo's nurses and they filed a complaint with the hospital's ethics committee. After three days, the family threatened to "take this to court." Jo's father stated his frustration, "Jo filled out this advance directive according to this organization's policy. We shouldn't have to take this to court! I'm the designated healthcare proxy and I'm acting in accord with what Jo wants. There's no reason why we should have to go through the hassle of getting a court order to get Dr. M to comply with Jo's advance directive. Doesn't the hospital have an obligation to adhere to its stated guidelines? What kind of organization is this?"

17

"But She Said . . ."

Sue McCoy

Mr. Milton is a seventy-three-year-old man with a newly diagnosed lung cancer. After conferring with his medical oncologist and radiation oncologist, he agrees to a trial of radiation and chemotherapy designed to shrink the tumor before its surgical removal. His surgeon, using pictures, explains to him that chemotherapy is administered through a "central venous line" or catheter into the largest vein in the body, the superior vena cava that carries blood directly to the heart. For convenience, access to the vena cava is gained through the skin with a needle into a one-inch silicone and metal diaphragm or port that is buried beneath the skin on the chest wall below the clavicle. This port is connected to a catheter, which is threaded into the subclavian vein that runs behind the clavicle and empties into the vena cava in the chest.

Although the surgeon may work through a small incision in the skin, she must locate the subclavian vein blindly with a small needle before introducing the larger catheter into this vein. The accuracy of such a "blind" search depends on the surgeon's experience and knowledge of anatomy. With the use of plain x-ray, an experienced surgeon can confirm the direction of the introducer and catheter but not the structures involved (other than bone). Once in place, the port and catheter can be used for chemotherapy, for other medications, and for intravenous nutrition should it become necessary during the chemotherapy.

The surgeon documents in the patient's medical record that she explained the procedure for placement of the port and the standard alternatives to Mr. Milton, who agrees, "This is the way to go." The surgeon is on her way to surgery and asks Mr. and Mrs. Milton to visit the nurse, who will explain the common risks associated with the procedure. She explains that the hospital requires that Mr. Milton sign a consent form indicating that he is aware of the benefits and risks of the procedure.

The hospital has recently undergone a shortage of experienced nursing staff. The hospital has downsized and, unfortunately, cuts in staff went deeper than originally intended. Although the surgeon's nurse is willing to speak to Mr. Milton, she is young and relatively inexperienced.

Mr. Milton's port and catheter placement is scheduled in the operating room to ensure sterile technique and to allow confirmation of the position of the catheter with x-ray during the procedure. The resident helping the surgeon in the operating room experiences some difficulty inserting the catheter into the vein, so the surgeon tries to place it. Because every patient has a slightly different anatomy, it is not unusual for surgeons to require several attempts to thread the catheter. At some point the catheter perforates Mr. Milton's superior vena cava, causing major bleeding into the chest. A chest surgeon comes quickly from an adjacent operating room and tries to control the bleeding through a thoracotomy incision, while the anesthesiologist and the surgeon help to maintain Mr. Milton's blood pressure with transfusions. Despite their best efforts, the patient develops a coagulopathy (inability to form normal blood clots) and exsanguinates and dies in the operating room.

The day after Mr. Milton's death, Mrs. Milton tells the hospital administrator that she and her husband had understood that the placement of a subcutaneous venous port was a simple procedure that only took an hour. She says that no one told them "that he could die from something that was supposed to help him live longer. We never would have agreed to it, no matter how many times the nurse said the surgeon had done it."

The hospital administrator notes from the patient's records that the surgeon spent twenty minutes with Mr. and Mrs. Milton explaining the procedure and answering questions about it. He notes that the surgeon's nurse had signed the consent form testifying that she informed the patient of the risks of surgery as required by hospital policy, which states that the "attending physician or his/her designee must inform the patient (or appropriate surrogate) of the common risks of the proposed intervention." The administrator knows that this particular nurse has a good reputation as being competent and thorough. Nevertheless, he wonders whether the nurse is familiar enough with the risks associated with this intervention to inform patients adequately about them.

18

First Child

James J. Finnerty

Mr. and Mrs. H were joyfully awaiting the birth of their first child. At the time, Mrs. H was an executive secretary in a prominent midwestern oil firm and Mr. H was a real estate developer. She was thirty-two years old, and he was thirty-eight.

When she was twenty-three weeks pregnant, Mrs. H ruptured membranes spontaneously. She was admitted to the maternity service of a large, multifaceted hospital owned by a healthcare chain. Chorioamnionitis (an inflammatory process potentially fatal to both mother and child) developed, and Mrs. H's labor could not be arrested.

The obstetrical staff counseled the couple on the dire prognosis for an infant born at twenty-three weeks gestation. Staff outlined the probability that the child would be born with severe retardation, intraventricular hemorrhage, blindness, cerebral palsy, and a variety of other problems. The couple was devastated and asked that the child not receive resuscitative intervention when it was born. A staff member entered a note into the hospital chart describing the couple's decision and indicating the concurrence of the obstetrical staff.

Mr. H left the hospital to arrange for a funeral and buy a burial plot. When he returned to the hospital, he was asked to attend a conference with his wife and medical and administrative staff. He and his wife were informed that hospital staff could not withhold resuscitative efforts when the child was born—that hospital policy that mandated resuscitative intervention would be given no matter what the circumstances. Mr. H inquired further about the hospital policy, he was told that the hospital's mission statement contained the clause, "This hospital shall endeavor to enhance and protect human life to the best of its ability." Mr. H answered, "But I see all over the hospital a listing of 'Patients Rights,' which includes the right of the patient or an appropriate surrogate to make all healthcare decisions for himself, including the right to refuse any and all treatments. We are legitimately refusing treatment for our unborn child in the child's best interest." The hospital attorney and administrative staff argued that the clause in the mission statement took precedence. Mr. H argued that the patients rights statement was meaningless under these conditions.

Delivery was imminent. Mrs. H could not be moved, and there was no time to pursue the matter in court. Hospital leaders, including both medical personnel and administrators, were adamant. The couple had no choice but to accept the decision of the hospital.

A female infant was delivered several hours later. She proved to be, as predicted, twenty-three weeks of gestation. Unfortunately, all of the other dire predictions were also fulfilled. On the second day of the infant's life, she experienced a severe intracranial hemorrhage. Multiple surgical procedures were necessary, but the infant survived. Seven months later, she was discharged from the hospital

The child is now seven years old and totally incapacitated. She cannot see, has severe spasticity, has urinary and fecal incontinence, cannot speak or respond to spoken words, and demands total and intensive supportive care.

19

If the Truth Be Known

Cynthia M. Jordan

Mr. Striker, diagnosed with lung cancer and metastasis to the brain, is admitted to the oncology unit following seven days of shortness of breath, coughing up blood, and periods of confusion. He is confused and very agitated. Hospital staff members determine that he is at high risk for falls.

The attending physician orders Ativan (an antianxiety agent) to help control Mr. Striker's agitated behavior. It is prescribed at a minimal dose, but it has a lingering effect on Mr. Striker. He remains lethargic for several hours after receiving the medication.

Mr. Striker's lethargy concerns his wife and family, so they are adamant that he is not to receive this medication. They communicate their wishes in no uncertain terms to the nursing staff. In turn, the supervising shift nurse speaks to the attending physician, who tells her that it is hospital policy to honor the wishes of the family.

In the late afternoon, Mr. Striker's agitation and confusion worsen. He tries to climb out of bed. The nurse is unable to control Mr. Striker's behavior and realizes that he may be a danger to himself unless he is constantly supervised.

The supervising shift nurse does not have extra staff available to provide continual supervision to Mr. Striker. She calls the patient's wife and explains the situation. Since she cannot provide around-the-clock supervision of Mr. Striker without jeopardizing the care of other patients, he must be given Atavin immediately, and there is still a doctor's order for it on Mr. Striker's chart.

Mrs. Striker is outraged. She exclaims, "I have no interest in your other patients! I am interested in my husband's welfare. I want him taken care of and you are not doing it."

20

Mother Knows Best

Walter A. Davis

Mrs. Kelly is a ninety-six-year-old woman who is admitted to a local hospital with the acute onset of slurred speech and weakness of the left arm and leg. She has a history of hypertension, coronary artery disease, and two previous strokes (both of which left her with only mild deficits). Mrs. Kelly had been living independently until approximately one year ago, when her overall mobility began to decline and she was unable to care for herself without help. She was placed in two different skilled nursing facilities over the course of the year, but she and her family were dissatisfied with the care she received at both places.

Following admission to the local hospital with her most recent stroke, her clinical status declines and she is unresponsive to voice and touch, although her vital signs are stable and she is breathing on her own. Dr. Walden, a neurologist sees her. He tells the family that her stroke has extended, and that she has a very poor prognosis for meaningful recovery. He believes that death is imminent. He asks the daughter, who has documented healthcare power of attorney status, to agree to transfer Mrs. Kelly to the hospice unit of the hospital, where the patient will receive comfort care only. The daughter agrees, and the patient's extended family all seem satisfied with this plan.

After two days on the hospice unit, Mrs. Kelly is sitting up in bed with help, takes small sips of water and pureed foods, and appears to recognize family members. She remains confused about basic orientation questions, but she does know that she has suffered a stroke and complains that her "arm and leg won't work." Both Dr. Walden and the patient's family are cautiously encouraged by the patient's progress, and they ask that she be given a trial of intensive therapy in a rehabilitation hospital.

In the rehabilitation hospital, a speech therapist does a full evaluation of Mrs. Kelly's swallowing function and determines that she is at significant risk of aspiration with oral feeding. A gastrostomy tube is recommended for all feeding, hydration, and medications. The patient's daughter refuses this, stating that her mother would not want to be fed through a tube and "kept alive that way." The patient is not able to communicate effectively that she understands the need for the tube, but she does say, "I don't want that," when asked directly if she would agree to the procedure.

The attending rehabilitation physician, Dr. Donagh, explains that the nurses and other hospital staff are not allowed to feed a patient with severe swallowing dysfunction because of the risk of aspiration and pneumonia. The daughter insists that the staff feed her mother and says that she will "accept the risk." Neither the daughter nor other family members are available to feed Mrs. Kelly themselves while she is in the hospital. The family feels that the intensive therapy is helping Mrs. Kelly, and they do not want her moved to another facility. They suggest having a home health nurse come to the hospital to feed her.

The family contacts a local home health agency owned by the hospital and ask if one of the staff nurses could come to the hospital and feed Mrs. Kelly. The director of the home health agency says that, although she would be willing to arrange for such service, the hospital administrator will not allow her to do so.

After numerous complaints by the staff nurses and therapists, Dr. Donagh transfers the patient to a local nursing home with the reluctant cooperation of the family. After admission to the nursing home, Mrs. Kelly is fed orally by nursing assistants who are not trained to feed patients with swallowing problems. After two days, the patient dies of aspiration pneumonia.

21

Mr. Chilton's Departure

Christopher W. Fuerst

Mr. Chilton, sixty-six years old, is admitted to the intensive care unit (ICU) with theophylline toxicity after taking three times the normal dose for approximately a week. On presentation to the ICU he is unresponsive and in renal failure. He requires intubation, mechanical ventilation, and continuous dialysis. He has heart dysrhythmias and requires maximal support.

Further investigation reveals the source of Mr. Chilton's toxic overdose. Mr. Chilton's physician prescribed the wrong dose of this drug after the patient's heart surgery two months ago. Mr. Chilton is now back at the same institution where he had his heart surgery. The investigation of this overdose reveals a complete system breakdown. The resident physician ordered three pills, three times a day instead of one pill, three times a day. The discharge nurse did not notice the mistake and, when discharging the patient, told him to take three pills, three times a day. The pharmacy did not notice the error and filled the prescription. Mr. Chilton went home and began taking one pill, three times a day.

Mr. Chilton's problems begin after a follow-up visit to his house by a home-health nurse. After reviewing his chart and medicine schedule, she asks him about the theophylline. He tells her he is taking one pill, three times a day, just as he had before his surgery. She tells him the prescription instructs him to take three pills, three times a day. The patient complies and overdoses.

Mr. Chilton's son is his surrogate decision maker while he is critically ill. The son becomes aware of the mistake immediately after Mr. Chilton's admission to the ICU. Mr. Chilton spends more than three months in the ICU and cannot be weaned from the ventilator. He undergoes a tracheostomy and is transferred to the stepdown unit. He fails further weaning attempts in the stepdown unit. It is agreed that nursing home placement is needed. By this time, Mr. Chilton regains decision-making capacity and is told what has happened to him.

The hospital's chief administrator and the chief of the medical staff meet to discuss the case. They agree that the hospital should be responsible for Mr. Chilton's care for this problem. They believe that it is the hospital's responsibility and that it is the right thing to do. They ask the head nurse to communicate this decision to Mr. Chilton and his son. The head nurse explains the decision of the chief administrator and chief of the medical staff, "Mr. Chilton will be taken care of by the hospital at no expense to him."

The hospital writes off Mr. Chilton's care. Time passes and it is clear that Mr. Chilton will remain ventilator dependent and that he will be better served in a nursing home. Mr. Chilton and his son agree that he would be happier in a nursing home. The son meets with the chief administrator and attending physician to discuss the case. The chief administrator advises the son to persuade Mr. Chilton, who has acquired considerable wealth throughout his career, to sign over his assets to his son. He advises the son to apply for Medicare and Medicaid to cover the cost of his father's care in the nursing home. The son is surprised and asks, "Won't the hospital be responsible?"

The chief administrator is puzzled, "But we never said that we would be responsible for Mr. Chilton's care outside the hospital."

22

Mr. Edward's Dilemma

William T. Warmath

Mr. Edward is sixty-three years old. He is admitted through the hospital emergency room on Friday evening, where he is placed on a ventilator before he is sent to the intensive care unit (ICU). His admitting diagnosis is acute respiratory failure with a history of chronic obstructive pulmonary disease and acute asthma. He is a widower with three children—John, Kent, and Julie. He is unemployed because he is disabled with his respiratory problems. He lives with his brother Sam on the outskirts of town. It is Sam who heard him knocking on the bedroom wall in the early hours of the evening in a frenzy to get his breath. Sam found him on the floor in a semiconscious state and immediately called 911.

Mr. Edward has executed a living will, as well as a healthcare power of attorney. His son John is his agent as listed on the power of attorney. The family arrives at the hospital several hours after Mr. Edward's admission. They find him on a respirator and in an unconscious state. John is outraged and speaks harshly to the nurse, "Why is my Dad on a respirator? Don't you know he has a living will and also a healthcare power of attorney?" The nurse states that the patient had no documents with him when he arrived at the unit, and she had not seen any other family member at the ICU.

Dr. Sherman, a pulmonologist and intensive care specialist, hears the noise and checks to see what is happening with his patient. Dr. Sherman is angry at the disturbance in the ICU. John tries to talk to Dr. Sherman, who indicates that he has nothing to discuss with the patient's son. John is unable to get Dr. Sherman to agree to a meeting later in the day.

Later, after Dr. Sherman has left, the nurse explains to John that the hospital offers ethics consultation services. She tells him that it is hospital policy to allow patients, surrogates, or family members to request a consultation at any time and that often some agreement about a plan of care can be reached through this process. John immediately calls the number given to him by the nurse and is told that the ethics consultant is away for the weekend and to call again on Monday.

John turns to the nurse and tells her that he does not want to wait forty-eight hours to begin a process that could result in further delays. He states that Mr. Edward would not want to wait that long.

23

Rural County Conflict

Amanda Beth Fulmor

In 1990, Rural County Hospital underwent an expansion, which included the addition of a new birthing center. Since its completion, Rural County Hospital delivers the vast majority of the county's babies and provides prenatal and postnatal care and obstetrics and gynecology services.

The management of this for-profit hospital intends to ensure that that the new birthing center meets two primary goals: (1) to provide competent and caring medical services to all children and mothers in Rural County and (2) to be economically viable. Consistent with the hospital's vision, the center recruits and hires physicians and nurses with excellent credentials and reputations. It amasses the resources and technology needed to serve all of the projected births within Rural County for the next decade. Hospital managers look for and initiate policies to ensure the birthing center's profitability. One such policy forbids any nurse associated with the hospital to help in home births.

Rural County contains a large Mennonite community. Mennonites generally believe that pregnancy and childbirth are a natural phenomenon and that a successful delivery, under normal circumstances, does not require high-tech medical interventions. Mennonite women prefer using a midwife to provide needed prenatal care and assist in the birthing process, thus avoiding what they view as the high-stress environment of the birthing center.

The Mennonites in Rural County oppose the new policies initiated by hospital management. The hospital refers Mennonite women who call for assistance from midwifes to an out-of-state practice. This practice eventually agrees to deliver all of the babies within the county's Mennonite community. Unfortunately, the distance between the out-of-state practice and Rural Couty is a problem for many of the Mennonite women—especially at the time of delivery. On several occasions, the midwife does not arrive at the home until after the baby is born. Neither the midwifes nor the Mennonite community view this arrangement as satisfactory or safe.

24

The Case of M.K.

James J. Finnerty

M.K. is sixty-five years old. He is a prominent and popular obstetrician-gynecologist in a suburban community. He combines an engaging personality and handsome appearance. His spouse, a former fashion model from a socially prominent family, is equally attractive. The couple has three children, who are all successful in their chosen fields.

In 1993 M.K. completed a living will instructing that treatment to prolong his dying should be withheld in the event of incurable or irreversible mental or physical condition. Specifically, he indicated that he wanted treatment withheld if he had a coma, persistent vegetative state, brain damage, or brain disease. He clearly specified "that the condition need not be terminal." He named his wife as his designated surrogate decision maker in the event he became incapable of making his own decisions.

Two years later, M.K.'s nurse finds him in his office slumped over his desk. He is unconscious. Empty, unlabeled pill bottles surround him, and there are several suicide notes on his desk. One of these notes instructs those who find him that he is not to be resuscitated.

M.K. is rushed to the emergency room. State law authorizes treatment on an emergency basis for patients who have attempted suicide, so emergency room staff perform gastric lavage with poison-absorbing charcoal and institute ventilatory support because the patient has experienced respiratory failure. M.K. survives and is transferred to the intensive care unit (ICU).

After several days in the ICU M.K. is diagnosed as being in a persistent vegetative state. The living will that the patient had written is obtained, and his wife asks that M.K. be removed from the ventilator and given comfort care only. She feels that this is the only course that is in accordance with his wishes. The attending physician agrees.

Despite the dire prognosis, M.K. unexpectedly regains consciousness. He is able to answer yes or no to questions by squeezing a questioner's hand. He indicates he does not wish to receive intravenous fluids or ventilatory support. A psychiatrist assesses M.K. as not capable and suffering from severe cognitive deficits.

M.K.'s wife persists in demanding only comfort care for her husband. She explains repeatedly that this is what her husband desires, and that it is in his best interest since he has no chance for what he considers to be a meaningful life.

Ms Z, the chief executive officer (CEO) of the hospital, is notified. She promptly calls the hospital's attorney for advice. The attorney points out that the hospital has just settled a million-dollar malpractice suit, which has received a great deal of publicity. The attorney advises Ms Z to instruct the attending physician to ignore the living will and the directions of M.K.'s wife.

Ms Z is reluctant. "I don't like doing this. A part of our mission states that we support a patient's or surrogate's right to make decisions concerning care. If we override this patient's wishes we will not be adhering to our own mission, and I think it is clear what M.K. wants." The attorney is adamant, "If the hospital loses another lawsuit, it will cease to operate and your mission statements won't matter."

Ms Z reluctantly calls the attending physician and instructs him to continue treatment. M.K. develops severe respiratory distress and imminent cardiac arrest. He is resuscitated for the second time. M.K.'s wife is not consulted.

M.K. recovers well enough over the next few weeks to become ambulatory. He suffers a massive cerebrovascular accident while walking in the hospital corridor. He is left aphasic, vision impaired, and paralyzed. The hospital bills M.K.'s insurance company for approximately $600,000. His total bills are close to $750,000, and his wife is responsible for the balance.

M.K. is committed to long-term nursing home care. He is not expected to recover.

25

The Sercye Case

Bethany Spielman

Christopher Sercye, a fifteen-year-old Chicago boy, suffered gunshot wounds in May 1998 while playing basketball with his friends in an alley behind Ravenswood Hospital. His friends tried to get him into the hospital, but they were unable to transport him the last thirty-five feet. They sought help from the police, who were, coincidentally, at the hospital. The officers radioed for an ambulance, which would have taken the boy to a trauma center. When the ambulance did not arrive in six minutes, the hospital's emergency room (ER) personnel called 911. They also prepared for the boy's admission, although the ER was filled to capacity at the time and the hospital was not a trauma center. ER personnel did not bring the boy inside or assist him while he was on the street. After a few more minutes had elapsed, police officers grabbed a wheelchair and transported Sercye into the ER. Shortly thereafter, Sercye went into cardiac arrest and died. When asked why they did not help the boy earlier, ER personnel cited hospital policy that forbade them to leave the building.

The policy cited by ER personnel had been developed in order to give priority to patients already in the ER department and to protect ER personnel from becoming involved with or hurt by ongoing crimes. The policy was, on its face, consistent with the Emergency Medical Treatment and Active Labor Act (EMTALA). Under EMTALA, a hospital must screen any individual who comes to the emergency department seeking medical care and determine whether the person has an emergency medical condition. If the individual has an emergency medical condition, the hospital must either stabilize the medical condition or transfer the person to another medical facility in accordance with the law's transfer requirements. However, there is little clarity about an obligation to treat a patient who is not yet in the hospital. Despite Ravenswood's technical compliance with EMTALA, the U.S. Health Care Financing Administration (HCFA) threatened to exclude Ravenswood Hospital from participation in Medicare because of its failure to promptly screen and treat a patient, unless the hospital could provide credible evidence that it had restructured its policy.

The hospital quickly changed its no-leaving-the-premises policy, working closely with HCFA and the Illinois Department of Public Health. The president and CEO of Ravenswood summarized the new policy as follows: "If someone on or near the hospital campus is believed to need immediate medical assistance, our employees must call a special internal telephone number to report it. The call provides immediate access to an ER nurse and physician, who determine how best to treat the person. If personnel leave the ER, medical professionals from other parts of the hospital fill in."

Part Three

Organization Issues in Professional Ethics

26

Introduction to Organization Issues in Professional Ethics

Edward M. Spencer

INTEGRATING PROFESSIONAL ETHICS INTO THE ORGANIZATION ETHICS PROGRAM

For healthcare organization ethics to achieve its goals, a healthcare organization (HCO) must be acquainted with and involved in all the activities related to its ethical climate. This means that organization ethics must have support and direction from the highest levels of authority in an HCO (usually the board of directors); an organization ethics program must be able to consider and give advice concerning all activities related to the mission and values of the HCO and how well the mission and values define the ethical climate of the organization; and such a program must be able to oversee the processes of ethical consideration in the clinical, business and management, and professional arenas. This means that an organization ethics program must integrate the sometimes different perspectives of clinical ethics, business ethics, research ethics, and professional ethics. To function effectively, it must include each of these perspectives in its conversations, and must work to resolve significant differences among these perspectives, using the stated values of the organization as the source for its advice.

The inclusion of clinical ethics and business ethics as a legitimate responsibility of an organization ethics program has engendered little controversy. Most who have written about organization ethics have included under its aegis at least some aspects formerly considered as clinical ethics issues or business ethics issues. However, little has been written about integrating the traditional ethical perspectives of healthcare professionals (particularly physicians and nurses) into an organization ethics program. In *Organization Ethics in Health Care,* Spencer and colleagues argue that, for an organization ethics program to fulfill its mission, professional ethics must be included.[1] The authors even go so far as to suggest that individual HCOs of the future will by necessity be repositories for specific professional ethical guidelines that will define ethical patient care. They suggest that attempting to maintain global professional codes that have real meaning for healthcare practitioners in the future will be impossible unless the broad general guidelines contained in global codes are expanded and occasionally modified to reflect the values of the organization with which professionals are associated.

Many of the ethical issues for healthcare professionals of the future will be related to conflicts that occur because of the constraints on medical practice imposed by governmental regulations, managed care, and insurance restrictions; the necessity to consider economic issues as a part of healthcare decisions; and HCOs' policies, on which increasing amounts of the healthcare professional's practice time and activities are likely to be spent. Each of these issues affect and is affected by HCOs. Thus, professional ethics will become one of the important aspects of an organization ethics program, and attention to early integration of professional ethics into an overall organization ethics program is mandatory. For these reasons, we have included cases related to the obligations of healthcare professionals here, and believe the interface between the traditional obligations of the healthcare professional and the values of HCOs may be one of the most important areas of consideration by developing organization ethics programs.

THE STATE OF PROFESSIONAL ETHICS

Before beginning with the cases, let's briefly look at the present state of professional ethics and what this means to the future of medical practice and healthcare systems. We focus on today's physicians and nurses, since these professions have a long traditions, which lead to expectations that members of the profession will maintain a strong ethical basis for their work. However, newer clinical professions (hospital chaplains, social workers, healthcare executives, risk managers, and so forth) also have developed specific sets of stated obligations to their patients, colleagues, community, and, at times, their employer (the HCO). These stated obligations can be in conflict when the professional goals and the organization's goals are different. The following discussion applies to any profession involved in healthcare that has a code of professional ethics that defines a professional's obligations as existing beyond obligations to the employer or professional partner.

The historical ethical basis for the practice of medicine extends back to the Hippocratic School in Greece in the fourth and fifth centuries B.C.E.[2] Many of today's physicians at their medical school graduation pledge a modified Hippocratic oath, which defines the ideals and obligations of a good physician.[3] The Hippocratic School focused on the physician acting for the benefit of his or her patient and keeping the patient from harm, with a particular emphasis on confidentiality (similar to the obligation of a priest to maintain confidentiality). Since the time of the Hippocratic School, there have been a number of additions and modifications to the expected obligations of a physician. Until very recently, however, the primacy of each individual patient's welfare was the major obligation of the physician, and this obligation was represented in the modern codes promulgated by physician organizations. The ethical basis for nursing extends back to the time of Florence Nightingale and, until recently, a nurse was also expected to act in the best interest of her patient.[4] This obligation supersedes an obligation to a nurse's employer or to a physician, even though the nurse could be working directly for an HCO or a physician.

Recently, a number of issues—particularly those associated with managed care—have challenged the relevance and the applicability of the professional codes of ethics. These conflicts of obligations have called into question the real ethical basis for the practice of medicine and nursing (and other healthcare professions). Are healthcare professionals obligated to advocate for each of their individual patients without regard to others who may be in need of scarce resources, or is there an equal or greater obligation to conserve society's resources, even if this means that one or more individual patients would not receive the best treatment? What about complying with economic incentives to decrease the resources used for particular individual patients when it has been shown that care under these schemes may be less than optimal? What are the obligations of the medical and nursing staffs of an HCO to support the HCO in its decisions that affect the availability and cost of healthcare? Is a physician or nurse obligated to refer a patient to a low-cost, adequately trained specialist or a high-cost, superbly trained specialist?

These and similar questions that address issues concerning the ethical obligations of healthcare professionals in today's healthcare system are receiving attention by professional organizations and by prominent physicians and nurses. The American Medical Association (AMA) is considering revising its *Code of Medical Ethics*[5] to include guidance on how to respond to the type of problems mentioned above, but it is having difficulty finding simple guidelines that will be helpful to practicing physicians in a wide range of situations, each of which involves conflicts. Other physician organizations are struggling with the same issues without much success. The American Nurses Association (ANA) is also in the process of revising its *Code for Nurses* and is struggling with some of the same issues.[6] The tendency to date has been for these codes to advocate respecting the rights of the patient, informing the patient of the issue at hand, and letting the patient make the final decision. The emphasis upon the primary of the obligation to the individual patient seems to be decreasing, even though this obligation is still expected by most patients.

Close scrutiny leads to the conclusion that no simple code will be able to address these issues adequately for all healthcare professionals, be they physicians, nurses, social workers, chaplains, or healthcare executives. Often, the values and mission of an HCO will be more pertinent to professional ethical decisions than the necessarily broad guidelines of professional codes. We envision that professional codes will set the tone for ethical decisions, with an HCO's organization ethics program supplying the final direction. Only an integrated organization ethics program that includes professional ethics can undertake this task.

To help encourage those who are attempting to integrate professional ethics into their organization ethics program, we have included the following cases for consideration. These cases do not represent examples of isolated professional dilemmas, since, in the real healthcare world, problems seldom occur this way. These cases involve questions about the economic impact on professional obligations, questions about professional obligations to the community, and questions about appropriate allocation of resources such as the professional's time. We hope these cases will encourage thought and discussion of the important issues that arise because of real or perceived conflicts between a professional's obligation and his or her role in today's healthcare system.

NOTES

1. E.M. Spencer et al., *Organization Ethics in Healthcare* (New York: Oxford University Press, 2000), 69-91.

2. Hippocrates, *The Theory and Practice of Medicine* (New York: Philosophical Library, 1964).

3. J.C. Fletcher et al., ed. *Introduction to Clinical Ethics,* 2nd ed. (Hagerstown, Md.: University Publishing Group, 1997), 289.

4. N.J. Bishop and S. Goldie, *A Bio-Bibliography of Florence Nightingale* (London: International Council of Nurses, 1962).

5. Council on Ethical and Judicial Affairs of the American Medical Association, *Code of Medical Ethics, Current Opinions and Annotations* (Chicago: American Medical Association, 1996).

6. American Nurses Association, *Perspectives on the Code for Nurses* (Kansas City: American Nurses Association, 1985).

27

BB

Patricia Reams

BB is a five-year-old girl who suffered an anoxic (lack of oxygen) brain injury three years ago as a result of a near drowning. She did not receive rehabilitation immediately after the injury because she lacked health insurance. She lived at home with her mother for a year, until she was hospitalized at an acute-care facility for status epilepticus. The patient's seizures were reasonably well controlled by medication, and she was enrolled in Medicaid.

Shortly after BB was hospitalized, a Child Protective Services (CPS) referral was initiated because her mother was suspected of neglect. The referral was made because the child was found to have low levels of anticonvulsant in her blood.

The caseworker assigned to BB terminated her mother's parental rights, because she did not think that BB's mother had either the emotional or financial means to care for the child. However, the mother got a job while BB was hospitalized and appealed for custody of her daughter. The caseworker was encouraged with the mother's progress in establishing a stable environment and expected to return custody of BB to her mother within a few weeks.

BB was transferred to Children's Miracle Rehabilitation Hospital (CMRH) for assessment of rehabilitation potential. Meanwhile, Mrs. B changed her mind about wanting custody of her daughter. She knew that if she brought BB home, she would probably lose her job and be required to go back on welfare.

Unfortunately, attempts at rehabilitation have been unsuccessful. Because there are no discharge options, BB has remained at CMRH for two years. She is at a very low level of functioning. All extremities are spastic. She requires range-of-motion exercises to prevent contractures, but there is no evidence of volitional movement. She makes nonword vocalizations in response to some visual stimuli, but there has been no progression of this in the past two years. She is fed via a gastric tube. She has daily seizures despite anticonvulsants. She develops aspiration pneumonia approximately every three months, which clears promptly with antibiotics. BB's CMRH treatment team has recommended a therapeutic foster home placement, but social services is unable to find a placement for the child.

BB's physical therapist, Ms PT, has an overload of cases and feels that she is not giving adequate service to her clients. She determines that BB is not benefiting, and will not benefit, from her services. Ms PT requests that she stop giving routine services to BB three times a week. She suggests that she act as a consultant on the case; and she can easily instruct nurses and other staff to provide the routine care that BB needs. This arrangement would allow Ms PT additional time for clients whom she feels would benefit.

Ms PT brings her request to the treatment team. The case manager tells her that she cannot stop giving services. BB is a Medicaid patient and, in order for the child to remain at CMRH, she must receive weekly rehabilitation services. Because social services cannot find BB a placement, there is no alternative to hospitalization at CMRH, and CMRH cannot afford to lose the patient's Medicaid billing.

28

Co-Chairs Disagree

Myra J. Christopher

A relatively new ethics committee in a suburban hospital works hard to be called upon to provide ethics consultation. The multidisciplinary committee has co-chairs, a physician and a nurse-administrator, and there is generally an atmosphere of collegiality at their monthly meetings.

A social worker on the hospital's transitional care unit (TCU) contacts the physician-chair to request an ethics consultation. She informs the co-chair that six months ago the medical director of the TCU accepted a position as medical director of a local preferred provider organization (PPO). The PPO provides coverage for a significant portion of the hospital's patients. She is concerned because the PPO's case managers are participating directly in treatment planning. When conflict occurs, the TCU medical director intervenes and makes decisions. The social worker is concerned that this conflict of interest could possibly compromise patient care. The physician agrees to review the case in the ethics committee without consulting his colleague and co-chair, the nurse-administrator.

The committee meets to discuss the case. The nurse-administrator strongly objects to the committee's reviewing this case. She argues that the case would be more appropriately resolved at the administrative level. Other committee members are suspicious that the hospital's administration does not trust them to deal with sensitive issues. They point out that the committee has already accepted the case for review. They argue that if they fail to review the case the committee will be perceived as ineffective and controlled by hospital administration. This portrayal could jeopardize future referrals.

When the ethics committee is unable to reach a decision, the co-chairs agree with the committee to discuss the issue with the hospital's chief executive officer.

29

Come to Be Heard

Joan L. Murray

A large university hospital system in a southern city was ready to implement an organization ethics committee. In developing the committee, hospital leaders had taken great care to invite the participation of key leaders from relevant disciplines that provided services within the healthcare system. Leaders from the healthcare system established guidelines and policies that would govern their actions. In particular, they invited physicians from several large departments to serve on the committee.

The hospital had experienced several transitional forms of restructuring within the last five years. This restructuring had involved changes in the hospital's leadership, administrative structure, practice patterns, and staffing patterns. In particular, the hospital had eliminated many nursing positions and reduced the hours of other nurses. Clinicians, especially nursing staff, felt intense pressure to "do more with less." Nursing staff, who perceived that patients were "sicker," increasingly felt unable to deliver the standard of excellence expected by hospital leadership.

Not long after the announcement of the new organization ethics committee, the nursing supervisor for the geriatrics unit requested a consultation about staffing patterns in his unit. He was concerned about whether his staff could meet the standard of excellence deemed necessary to realize the hospital's stated values and mission. He had already stated his concerns to his unit head, who had told him that no resources were available and that he and his staff would have to "adjust."

Later that day, the nursing supervisor met with a physician associated with the geriatrics unit to discuss the care of one particular patient. The physician commented that he knew of the nursing supervisor's appearance before the organization ethics committee and applauded his decision to try to get the committee involved in some of the crucial issues facing the hospital.

The nursing supervisor left the meeting quite upset. He had been under the impression that his meeting with the organization ethics committee would remain confidential.

30

Doctor Will See You Now

Linda J. Keilman and Judith Andre

Mrs. Allen is a secretary who works in a small bank in a town dominated by a large medical center. She has a daughter who is affected by a behavioral disorder and who requires frequent visits to a pediatrician. Mrs. Allen is divorced and lives some distance from her family. She belongs to a support group for parents of children who have this disorder, which has symptoms that can range from relatively mild to very severe. She and other parents have been able to exchange information about the disorder and its effects on the children's behavior. Mrs. Allen wants to take advantage of all the resources she can in order to help her child, who suffers from a more extreme form of the disorder.

Mrs. Allen wishes that she and her child could have additional access to the pediatrician who oversees her daughter's case. The pediatrician, who is employed by the town's medical center, is generally regarded as a fine doctor and a conscientious research scientist who is interested in the ethics associated with certain types of research on children. Mrs. Allen has great respect for the medical center and believes that the pediatrician has her child's best interest at heart.

The medical center plays an active role in the community. It portrays itself as having even-handed, honest, and fair relationships with its various stakeholders (including its employees, staff, clinicians, and patients). The medical center promotes this perception through various strategies including policy statements, a sophisticated website, and sponsorship of local heath bazaars and charity events. It has an active public relations department, whose manager has close relationships in the local and state media.

Mrs. Allen must schedule her child's visits to the pediatrician three to four months in advance. One weekday morning, she is with her child in the waiting room of the pediatrician's office. She is worried because she has had to take the morning off, and she has used almost all of her "personal time"—a benefit that allows her to take off a certain amount of time per year at her own discretion. She is relieved that the fiscal year will soon be over and she will have another block of time at her disposal. She glances at her watch. She should have plenty of time to drop her daughter off with the babysitter and get to work by one o'clock.

The receptionist approaches Mrs. Allen and says, "I have to move your appointment back until early this afternoon. We have had an unexpected emergency, and the doctor has to see another patient first. You can have some coffee or a light lunch in the hospital cafeteria if you like." Mrs. Allen is upset but hopes that she can talk her boss into letting her make up the time lost through overtime work. She starts to collect her child and her belongings and head for the cafeteria.

Before Mrs. Allen can leave, Mrs. Carter and her child enter the pediatrician's waiting room. Mrs. Carter is a member of Mrs. Allen's support group, who has a child affected by a milder version of the disorder. The two women greet each other, but Mrs. Allen is puzzled. "I thought you saw a different pediatrician," she says. Mrs. Carter agrees, "I do, generally. But I forgot that he is out of town most of this month. We are going to Europe at the end of next week, and I wanted to make sure that I have enough medication for the trip. I don't want our vacation ruined by bad behavior."

Mrs. Allen is surprised. "It's not easy to get an appointment with my child's doctor. I have to make my appointments months in advance. How did you manage to get the appointment on such short notice?"

Mrs. Carter laughs, "Oh, I never have any trouble. My husband is a physician who works here at the medical center. All the doctors here are very good about seeing friends and family members of colleagues whenever they want to be seen, even if they have to reschedule other patients. It is a professional courtesy they extend to one another, and the medical center encourages them to continue this policy since the administration believes it enhances professional satisfaction at the center."

The receptionist approaches and, with a smile, invites Mrs. Carter and her child into an examination room. "Doctor will see you now," she says.

Mrs. Allen is furious. She is going to be late to work, and will have to work overtime. She turns to the receptionist and asks, "Is this the emergency that you told me about? It doesn't seem that urgent to me."

The receptionist nods, "Look, I know how you feel. But please don't make a fuss. There is nothing either you or I can do about it. The medical center looks after its own before it looks after others. I was told to reschedule and tell you it was an emergency." Mrs. Allen sits down, wondering if her health insurance plan will allow her to switch to a pediatrician who is not connected to the medical center.

31

Home Again, Home Again

Walter A. Davis

Healthy Valley Hospital is part of a tertiary-care, academic medical center in a small city in the Southeast. In response to negative publicity about the hospital's acquisition of a number of local family care practices, the public relations department recently issued several statements to the press in which the hospital declared: "Cost issues are not our first concern. Our first concern is the health of our patients."

In a routine audit, hospital administrators noticed that Medicare and third-party payers were increasingly denying payment for the last few days of hospital acute care for some patients on the hospital's orthopedic surgery floor. When they pulled the charts for the patients in question, they found that insurance providers were denying payment because the length of stay for these patients was two to three days longer than the average hospital stay for the diagnoses involved. These patients had been kept in the hospital longer because the physical therapy and nursing staff believed that the patients lacked sufficient stability with ambulation and self-care and needed more therapy before discharge to home.

Senior hospital administrators asked the administrator in charge of orthopedic services to draft a letter to the nursing and physical therapy staff, reminding them: "Safety and mobility concerns are most appropriately handled by home health agencies and are not a reason to keep patients in the hospital."

32

Kevin and the Military

Phillip Nieburg

A pediatrician is one of a dozen physicians assigned to a large military base within the United States. It is a period of international crisis. Many of the personnel on the base have been rotating to military bases overseas for six-month periods, with three months back at the base before their next overseas rotation.

One day, Mrs. B comes to see the pediatrician. Mrs. B, who has brought her children to this pediatrician before for routine health issues, is the wife of a sergeant currently assigned overseas. They have three children and live on the base. Their oldest child, eleven-year-old Kevin, has just been suspended from school for the second time for setting fires. He had been seen lighting matches in school early the previous week and had been warned by the teacher and principal, who had also spoken with his mother. Several days later, Kevin was caught setting fire to a pile of sticks on the playground and was suspended for a week. He had been allowed back in school just yesterday and was suspended again this morning after starting another fire in a janitor's closet.

The pediatrician first talks with Mrs. B while Kevin sits in the waiting room. Mrs. B is distraught. She tells the pediatrician that Kevin has always been a good student and that he has never been a behavior problem until about three weeks ago, beginning around the time when her husband left with only two days' notice for his third successive six-month overseas assignment. Because of the shortage of personnel with Sgt. B's technical skills (missile electronics), he was only allowed two weeks at home between rotations this time rather than the usual three months. His latest departure was the week before Kevin's birthday.

Kevin and his dad have had a close relationship, and the child was obviously upset at his father's short time at home and at his abrupt departure for another long absence. Since his father left, Kevin has lost his normal enthusiasm for school, and his schoolwork has suffered. Two weeks ago, he missed several days of school because of stomach aches. He is not eating well, is not interested in playing with his usual friends, and is spending many of his daylight hours lying in his bed.

The pediatrician talks at length with Kevin, who is polite but not very responsive. His only spontaneous conversation is his tearful recounting of what he sees as the injustice of his father's abrupt departure after only two weeks at home and about how the events have affected him. It appears to the pediatrician that Kevin is clinically depressed, a diagnosis that the base psychologist concurs with later that day. Given the severity of Kevin's symptoms and the threat represented by his acting out, the pediatrician and the psychologist agree that Sgt. B should be brought home as soon as possible. The pediatrician then discusses this option with Mrs. B, who clearly agrees with the assessment of the severity of the situation. Finally, at the end of the afternoon, the pediatrician discusses the situation with the hospital commander, also a physician. The hospital commander agrees to talk with Col. M, the unit commander, about the return of Kevin's father.

The next day, the hospital commander calls to inform the pediatrician that Col. M has discussed the issue with his staff and, unfortunately, decided that Kevin's father cannot be sent home now. There are no personnel with similar skills currently available to replace him, and the military situation where he is assigned is too critical to spare him at this time. Col. M hopes to have a replacement in two or three months.

Kevin's mother, who has begun counting on having her husband sent home, is very upset at this decision. She tells the pediatrician that she is going to discuss this situation with the base Red Cross representatives, who routinely act as patient advocates in situations such as this.

Later that day, the hospital commander calls the pediatrician in to tell him that Col. M has called and is clearly annoyed. The Red Cross representative has told Col. M that Kevin's mother says that the pediatrician has recommended that the child's father be sent home. (Col. M had been unaware that the pediatrician had already discussed this issue with Mrs. B). Although Col. M and the hospital commander agree that having his father home would perhaps be best for Kevin, they also agree that organizational priorities must take precedence in this instance.

Col. M asked the hospital commander to point out to the pediatrician politely but firmly that the pediatrician's responsibility as a military physician is to contribute to the mission of the organization. He is reminded that both his salary and his oath of office (military commission) obligate him to put the organization's priorities first, even when this may conflict with his perceived obligations to his patients. The pediatrician is asked not to discuss any similar diagnostic or treatment options with future patients or parents that might affect achieving military goals without discussing them with the hospital commander first.

33

Mildred's Case

Robert L. Potter

Mildred is ninety-two years old. She has suffered a series of strokes that have left her paralyzed and unable to make her own decisions. She lives in a nursing home, where she seems to enjoy sitting in a chair; she frequently becomes very agitated if kept in bed for prolonged periods of time. At the nursing home, she falls from a Hoyer lift while being transferred from bed to chair following a period of "extreme agitation" (as described in her chart). Mildred is admitted to the local hospital, which owns the nursing home, with a fractured left hip and right femur. Mildred's attending physician, who is also the medical director of the nursing home, contacts her oldest daughter, who is named in Mildred's advance directive as holding durable power of attorney for healthcare decisions (DPOA). After discussing Mildred's diagnosis and treatment plan, the physician and daughter agree to a do-not-resuscitate (DNR) order. Mildred's daughter is deeply uncomfortable with this decision but agrees that her mother's advance directive, which states that she does not want resuscitation attempted, should be honored. Three hours later, Mildred's son arrives at the hospital and demands that the DNR order be rescinded. The attending physician explains to the son that only the decision maker named in the DPOA has the authority to make such decisions and that, therefore, the DNR order will stand. Mildred's son is unhappy and vows to "take this matter all the way to the top."

One hour later, the hospital attorney calls the attending physician and suggests that it would be in everybody's interests to persuade the daughter to rescind the DNR order. He explains that the nursing home has the following policy: "Transferring an incapacitated patient from bed to chair shall be accomplished by at least two staff members. One member of the transferring team shall be certified in the latest transferring techniques as determined by the Director or Nursing." The son has learned that, at the time of Mildred's fall, she was being transferred by only one staff member. The son threatens to institute a lawsuit. The physician knows that recent cutbacks have left the nursing home short-handed and that, at the time of Mildred's fall, no other staff members were available to help with the transfer.

34

No Exceptions

Betty L. Newell

Dr. Sanders is a partner in an internal medicine group practice in an affluent town in the Northeast. He and his four partners established the practice three years ago. Recently, Dr. Sanders and his partners decided to refuse to accept additional Medicaid patients because low Medicaid reimbursement rates do not cover additional staff expenses generated by excessive paperwork.

Dr. Sanders is seeing one of his patients, Mrs. Andrews. She belongs to a number of organizations and clubs including the Junior League and Garden Club, is active in community fund-raising events, and has helped to establish a number of charity and educational outreach programs. Although Mrs. Andrews is only thirty-five years old, she is widely respected and very well liked in the community. She has made no secret of her admiration for Dr. Sanders and has referred her friends and associates to him. Her referrals have enabled the practice to grow much more quickly than it might have otherwise. Dr. Sanders knows that Mrs. Andrews is a well-intentioned and genuinely caring person. He is very fond of her and, since she is healthy, he very much enjoys her routine visits.

Mrs. Andrews asks Dr. Sanders if he will see a disabled friend of hers who has Medicaid. She has been unable to find a primary care physician for her friend, who has a range of complex medical problems. The closest physician who will agree to accept the patient is in the city twenty miles away. The patient does not drive, buses are terribly uncomfortable for her, and the single taxicab company in the town will not take Medicaid patients for routine appointments. Mrs. Andrews has been driving her friend, but with her schedule it has been difficult. Mrs. Andrews knows that Dr. Sanders's practice is refusing additional Medicaid patients. Nevertheless, she asks Dr. Sanders to accept her friend as a patient.

35

Physician Penalized for Appealing Treatment Denials

Brian O'Toole

A hospital system located in the center of a semi-rural state formed its own managed-care organization, called BestCare, in response to competitive pressures from the northern part of the state. BestCare is partially owned by the physicians employed by the hospital system (through an independent foundation owned by hospital physicians) and partially owned by the facilities associated with the system. Employees of all of the facilities owned by the hospital system receive their health insurance through BestCare. BestCare returns all but 8 percent of its net revenues to the foundation and the system facilities. The other 8 percent represents BestCare's administrative expenses. The amount of yearly bonuses received by physicians employed by the hospital system depends on BestCare's profitability.

An employee of the hospital system, an elderly and very timid woman who works in housekeeping, scheduled an appointment with her dermatologist, Dr. K. Dr. K made a routine telephone call to BestCare to get approval for surgical removal for what he believed to be pilar tumors on the patient's scalp. Dr. K received permission, but was explicitly instructed that BestCare would not approve payment for examination of the tumors by pathology. Dr. K argued that his patient was extremely fearful and needed reassurance and that, while chances were slim that the tumors were malignant, this request for pathology services was neither unreasonable nor expensive. He submitted a written appeal to BestCare, which was denied.

Dr. K felt strongly enough about the issue to send tissue samples away for examination at his own expense. He documented all of this thoroughly and sent copies to his local medical society.

A month later, Dr. K received a letter from BestCare informing him that he had not acted in a collegial manner with the organization, that he had been disrespectful of their appropriate roles, and that an "incident summary" was being lodged in the office of the hospital system's chief of medical staff. The incident summary would be used in Dr. K's annual performance evaluation and could serve as the basis for a reduction in his yearly bonus.

Dr. K wonders whether he should pursue the matter through the office of the chief of medical staff or whether, by so doing, he will simply make matters worse for himself.

36

Should I Report Dr. Jones?

Edward M. Spencer

Nurse Williams is concerned. She is the head nurse on the obstetrical unit of Smalltown Hospital, which means she is responsible for the overall operation of the hospital's entire obstetrical service including the operating rooms where cesarean sections (C-sections) are done. She has just returned from the surgical suite, where Dr. Jones just completed a C-section. While talking with Dr. Jones, Nurse Williams noted a slight odor of whiskey. Because she has heard rumors that Dr. Jones was previously admitted to an alcohol rehabilitation center, she decides to pursue the matter further.

Nurse Williams asks Nurse Stanley, Dr. Jones's assistant on the just completed C-section, to stop by before going home. During their meeting, Nurse Williams asks Nurse Stanley about Dr. Jones's competence and about any signs of his drinking. Nurse Stanley says that she believes Dr. Jones is the best obstetrician on the staff and that he is always professional and has never shown any signs of intoxication. As she is leaving, Nurse Stanley mentions that during the C-section Dr. Jones said that he had just come from a party because his partner—who was on call—was busy with another patient.

Nurse Williams checks the hospital policy concerning impaired professionals. It states, "If a professional associated with Smalltown Hospital is known to be impaired by drugs or alcohol to the extent that one or more patients may be in jeopardy, the person with such knowledge is required to report this information immediately." Nurse Williams knows of one other similar situation, which ended in the physician's dismissal without any offer of rehabilitation. So, she decides to talk with Dr. Jones rather than report her suspicions.

She confronts Dr. Jones the next morning at rounds, and he denies taking any alcohol before the C-section the previous night. He angrily tells Nurse Williams that she could be sued for slander if she pursues this matter further. Later she talks to her supervisor, the director of patient services, and tells her of the dilemma without naming names. Her supervisor advises dropping the matter immediately.

Part Four

Organization Issues in Research Ethics

37

Introduction to Organization Issues in Research Ethics

Ann E. Mills

THE RESEARCH MISSION OF
ACADEMIC HEALTH CENTERS

Academic health centers (AHCs)—medical schools, teaching hospitals, and other health science schools—provide healthcare services to patient populations. However, they have two important additional missions—teaching future generations of healthcare professionals and performing research to generate new knowledge. These missions increase the number of stakeholders affected, and so add an additional layer of complexity to decision-making processes in AHCs. But AHCs *are* healthcare organizations (HCOs) and, as such, they confront organizational challenges and make decisions that affect their missions and ethical climates.[1] These features of organizational life are the focus of this book.

We are unaware of any published argument for the inclusion of research ethics into the organization ethics programs of HCOs. We believe that this is due to two reasons. First, healthcare organization ethics is a relatively new field. Academics and professionals are only beginning to think about the implications of organizational ethics on the practical activities that determine the HCO's ethical climate—including activities associated with the research mission of AHCs. Second, many in the healthcare ethics community are already focused on the programs, regulations, and guidelines that exist to ensure that human subjects are protected from research risks.[2]

REFORMING AND EXPANDING

The case for reforming and expanding programs, regulations, and guidelines to oversee, monitor, and guide research on human subjects is obvious. The old research model has changed from that of one investi-

107

gator working at one institution controlling a discrete group of research patients, to that of groups of investigators working at many sites controlling large numbers of research patients who may be enrolled in multiple studies. The structure of research funding is changing as private sponsorship is increasing relative to federal sponsorship.[3] These changes in the scope of research activities and the structure of research funding generate challenges to existing regulations and guidelines that were not addressed when these regulations and guidelines were formulated.[4]

Federal organizations (including the U.S. Department of Health and Human Services—DHHS, the National Institutes of Health—NIH, and the U.S. Food and Drug Administration—FDA, and private industry—the biotechnology and pharmaceutical industries) are aware of the increasingly sophisticated ethical concerns generated by the scope and structure of current research and are seeking ways to meet these challenges. For instance, the NIH has implemented some of the recommendations made to its Director's Advisory Committee on the organizational locus of the Office of Protection from Research Risks (OPRR)[5] and the authority it should have to carry out its mission.[6] (Until June 2000, OPRR was the oversight mechanism that existed to protect animal and human subjects from research risks associated with projects funded in whole or in part by the NIH.)

In June 2000, OPRR was renamed the Office for Human Research Protections (OHRP) and relocated from NIH to DHHS, reporting to the Assistant Secretary for Health. The OHRP has compliance and oversight responsibilities, a coordinating role within the government, and the responsibility to negotiate assurances (that is, pledges assuring ethical conduct) with institutions involved in human research. It also has the responsibility to provide guidance, through education programs concerning human subject research, to evaluate the effectiveness of DHHS policies and programs for the protection of research subjects, and to enhance and improve methods to avoid unwarranted risks to humans participating as subjects.[7]

Institutional review boards (IRBs) have the responsibility to approve and monitor the way in which research is carried out in their organizations. Federal agencies are concerned about the effectiveness of this mechanism. Reports issued by the DHHS Office of the Inspector General show concern about the vulnerability of local IRBs in a changing research setting.[8] Follow-up reports and recommendations for reform of IRBs have been made.[9] In May 2000, DHHS issued a press release saying that it plans to take an aggressive approach to addressing the education of persons who are associated with IRBs, informed consent issues, and monitoring human research. Addressing these issues will mean improved coordination between the FDA, the NIH, and IRBs. In addition, DHHS is seeking to find ways to address conflict-of-interest issues. It is also pursuing legislation to authorize civil fines for violations of informed consent and other important research principles. Such fines would range from $250,000 per clinical investigator up to $1 million per research institution.[10]

The Biotech Industry Organization (BIO), an organization representing the nongovernmental biotechnology industry, has formed a standing committee on bioethics to define, articulate, and communicate the industry's positions and standards of conduct on major bioethical issues.[11] In addition, the Pharmaceutical Research and Manufacturers of America (PhRMA), an organization of approximately 100 U.S. companies that have a primary commitment to pharmaceutical research, has developed position papers on important ethical issues in research and healthcare.[12]

However, updated federal regulations and guidelines and concern with ethical questions by private industry are not enough to provide or sustain a sensitive ethical climate within AHCs. AHCs *already* agree to act toward their research subjects in a manner consistent with agreed-upon principles.[13] The principles on which new recommendations are made have not changed—only their applicability.

LINKING IRBs TO
ORGANIZATION ETHICS PROGRAMS

The specific applicability of these principles to an institution is monitored by an AHC's IRB. However, because IRBs function in institutional contexts, they cannot be effective without the wider support and interest of their institutions and its leaders. One reason such widespread attention is being paid to updating regulations and guidelines is the perception that AHCs do not take seriously their responsibility to act in a manner that is consistent with agreed-upon principles. A manifestation of this lack of interest is the widespread perception that AHCs do not adequately support their IRBs—that often IRBs lack the staff, the time, and the resources needed to appropriately study, approve, and monitor research carried out under their institutions' auspices.

Because organization ethics programs are concerned with the positive ethical climate of their organizations, they must also be concerned with the procedures and processes that support this atmosphere in AHCs. The success or failure of an IRB in overseeing the practical applicability of research ethics in research with human subjects will be a part of the overall ethical climate of an AHC. Because research is a process by which an AHC achieves an important part of its mission, its IRB should be involved with the organization ethics program. This should apply regardless of the structure or geographic location of the IRB and regardless of the size of the institution's research budget in comparison with its overall budget.[14]

We see no disadvantage to AHC's implementing this link between the IRB and the organization ethics program. On the contrary, the inclusion of IRB members in the organization ethics program can work to the advantage of the IRB, the ethics program, and the AHC. It will allow persons involved in the organization ethics program to develop a perspective that includes the ethical principles that should guide research on vulnerable subjects and allow them to act as a knowledgeable resource for AHC leaders who must negotiate complex transactions with both internal and external stakeholders. It will widen the perspective of IRB members and will allow the IRB to serve as the visible and respected vehicle that applies the AHC's mission and values to a specific and practical use in the area of human research.

INCLUDING RESEARCH ETHICS AS PART OF AN ORGANIZATION'S OVERALL ETHICAL CLIMATE

AHCs, along with other HCOs, are charged by the Joint Commission on Accreditation of Healthcare Organizations (JCAHO) to develop a code of ethics. This code can embrace and support research ethics as part of the values through which an AHC achieves its missions of patient care, teaching, and research. Because an organization ethics program will develop the ethical atmosphere of the organization through educational and communication activities, this wider perspective can be disseminated throughout the organization via the channels already in place. The visible inclusion of research ethics as part of an institution's overall ethical climate will go far in reassuring internal and external stakeholders that the institution means what it says about protection of research subjects. It will add to an institution's credibility at a time when national attention is focusing on of institutional attitudes toward research subjects.

Media reports of cases involving real or perceived abuse of research subjects have become commonplace. The number of recent cases and the scope of violations of current regulations by well-respected and nationally known AHCs suggest that voluntary oversight through local IRBs may not be sufficient to ensure the safety and well-being of research subjects. Hence, the case for updating federal regulations and guidelines governing human research is urgent and legitimate, as well as sad and disappointing. The case for reform through federal legislation rests on the perception that AHCs have not implemented or supported the values they have said that they endorse. But voluntary or involuntary compliance with expanded federal reforms will not guarantee to the public or to research subjects that the AHC acts in accordance with its own stated values.

In the general introduction to this book, we asked readers who are analyzing the cases it includes to assume that HCO leaders are committed to maintaining and enhancing the ethical climate of the organization. We have emphasized that, in the absence of such a commitment, the activities of any one person or committee to develop, enhance, or maintain a positive ethical climate in an HCO will be ineffective. This condition for success has been amply demonstrated in some of the cases that have claimed national attention: IRBs are ineffective in their work without the support of their institutions.

The cases in this section illustrate the changing environment of AHCs and the some of the resulting ethical dilemmas faced by AHCs and their stakeholders. The cases illustrate the enormous challenges faced by leaders of AHCs to maintain and enhance their missions and the uncertain ethical climate that may result from decisions made in response to these challenges. Most of the cases in this section are based on news articles and the direct experience of contributing authors who work in the research environment. In all of these cases, as in the other sections of this book, there is a clear role for a functioning organization ethics program—a role that sustains the ethical atmosphere of the organization while providing practical guidance within the framework of the organization's mission.

NOTES

1. H. Pardes, "The Perilous State of Academic Medicine," *Journal of the American Medical Association* 283, no. 18 (2000): 2427-9. See also M. Angel, "Is Academic Medicine for Sale?" *New England Journal of Medicine* 342, no. 20 (2000): 1516-8; C.C. DeAnelis, "The Plight of Academic Health Centers," *Journal of the American Medical Association* 283, no. 18 (2000): 348-9.

2. J.D. Moreno et al., "Updating Protections for Human Subjects Involved in Research," *Journal of the American Medical Association* 280, no. 22 (1998): 1951-8.

3. Although the NIH's budget has more than doubled in the past ten years, its share of total health research and development (R&D) expenditures in the United States has decreased from about 35 percent in the mid-1980s to about 29 percent today. Over the same period, the share of total health R&D expenditures coming from non-federal sources has increased from 34 to 43 percent. More information can be found at <http://www.nih.gov/ofm/budget/fy2001Pressbriefing.htm>.

4. See note 1 above.

5. NIH-funded research projects involving animal or human subjects are subject to oversight provided by the Office of Protection from Research Risks (OPRR), a program established within the NIH in 1972. This office has been moved to DHHS and renamed.

6. See note 2 above. Former DHHS Secretary Donna E. Shalala accepted the committee's recommendation and directed that OPRR be relocated to the Office of Public Health and Science within the Office of the Secretary. In addition, she directed that the position of director of the OPRR be upgraded to senior executive service level, that resource needs of the elevated office be reviewed as part of the relocation, and that a new advisory committee on protection from research risks be created. Further information can be found at <http://www.hhs.gov/news/press/1999pres/991104c.html>.

7. In spite of the broader functions and increased visibility of the OHRP, it has not been given the authority that the OPRR had to interdict federally sponsored research funds at an institution if regulations are violated. Rather, the OHRP's Division of Compliance Oversight "recommends remedial or corrective action as necessary to agency or Department officials as appropriate." *Federal Register* 65, no. 114 (13 June 2000): 37136.

8. In June 1998, the office issued *Institutional Review Boards: A Time for Reform*. It can be found at <http://waisgate.hhs.gov/cgi-bin/waisgate? WAISdoc ID=0562319628+43+0+0&WAISaction=retrieve>.

9. On 20 April 1999, the DHHS Office of the Inspector General issued a follow-up report, *Protecting Human Research Subjects: Status of Recommendations.* The report emphasizes that few of the recommendations made in the 1988 report (*Institutional Review Boards: A Time for Reform*) have been implemented. The 1999 report can be found at <http://grants.nih.gov/grants/oprr/oprr.htm>.

10. DHHS Press Release, 20 May 2000. DHHS Press Office: (202)690-6343.

11. The Biotech Industry Organization (BIO) estimates that there are 819 companies in an industrywide total of 1,283 companies working on therapies or cures for diseases that affect large numbers of people. Product sales for the industry in 1998 were $13.4 billion. In 1997, appropriately 30 percent of product sales represented human health products. In 1998, the industry spent $9.9 billion on R&D. In the United States there are more than 350 biotechnology drug products and vaccines currently in human clinical trials and hundreds more in early development. More information about BIO can be found at <http://www.bio.org/govt/facts.html>. For a description of the BIO's position on ethical issues and a description of the board, go to <http://www.bio.org/bioethics/bioethics_intro.html>.

12. PhRMA estimates that research-based pharmaceutical companies will invest $26.4 billion in R&D in 2000, a 10.1 percent increase over 1999. These expenditures include $22.4 billion spent within the United States by both U.S.-owned and foreign-owned firms, plus an additional $4.0 billion spent abroad by U.S.-owned firms. Research-based companies have more than tripled their R&D expenditures since 1990. More information about PhRMA can be found at <http://www.phrma.org/index.htm

For position papers issued by PhRMA on ethical issues in research, see <http://www.phrma.org/issues/index.html>.

13. Federal policy dictates that, before an institution can conduct any human research, it must provide a written assurance that it will comply with federal policy mandates on human research. This mandate directs that an institution involved in biomedical or behavioral research should have in place a set of principles and guidelines that govern the institution, its faculty, and its staff in the discharge of its responsibilities for protecting the rights and welfare of hu-

man subjects taking part in research conducted at, or sponsored by, the institution, regardless of the source of funding. See *Code of Federal Regulations* 46, subpart A, section 46.

14. A survey conducted by the American Medical Association and published in the *Journal of the American Medical Association* reviewed the revenue-supporting activities and programs of the 125 accredited medical schools in the United States from 1995-1998. Revenue to AHCs is derived from three major sources: practice plans, contracts and grants, and hospital support. Grant and contract revenue constituted the second largest source of support (29.5 percent of total revenue). But an analysis of trends suggests that the sum of revenues from practice plans and hospital support is declining. See J.K. Krakower, D.J. Williams, and R.F. Jones, "Review of U.S. Medical School Finances, 1997-1998," *Journal of the American Medical Association* 282, no. 9 (1999): 847-54. Available at <http://jama.ama-assn.org/issues/v282n9/full/jsc90199.html>.

38

A Matter of Days

Paul A. Lombardo

Pharmacom is a manufacturer and distributor of prescription and over-the-counter medications. The company is ready to exploit its recent success in developing and marketing a drug to treat arthritis. A stock offering has been prepared, and a consortium of well-respected investment bankers has agreed to underwrite it. A formal agreement and announcement to Wall Street is expected within a matter of days. This offering is expected to raise the capital needed to build new facilities and hire new staff in order to expand Pharmacom's research and development (R&D) activities.

Pharmacom's expansion plans include research collaboration with a prominent eastern academic health center. The center welcomes this initiative. During the past five years, the center's revenues have decreased as a result of managed-care competition and federal and state cost-control legislation. The president of the center knows that, without this collaboration, the center has a real chance of failing within the next few years.

Bob Watson is Pharmacom's newly hired director of R&D. He has spent twenty years as a practicing physician and research scientist at the University Health Center. He maintains a faculty appointment at the center concurrently with his position at Pharmacom. The Pharmacom-university agreement specifies several joint faculty-industry positions and a university seat on Pharmacom's executive committee. Incentive payments will be used to reward scientists and administrators involved in successful drug development. Pharmacom and the university will share the profits that result from any collaborative project.

Bob has *carte blanche* to improve the quality of Pharmacom's research efforts as the foundation for new product development. As a first step, he decides to familiarize himself with Pharmacom's R&D history. He has his assistant pull the research division's quarterly reports for the entire ten years of the company's existence. Bob is especially eager to learn the story of Artharex. Artharex, the best selling anti-inflammatory drug marketed by Pharmacom for relief from arthritis, is the company's biggest success. Artharex is the reason why expansion through a stock offering is possible.

Bob learns that in Pharmacom's third year, Artharex was tested on a series of animals, including dogs and mice, to determine its potential toxicity. The graphs plotted during those tests showed that the drug produced no unexpected events in mice, but one of the dogs tested died soon afterward. In the small print of the footnotes, Bob learns that the cause of death was cardiovascular failure. Researchers judged that the death of the dog was unrelated to the drug.

Bob's curiosity pushes him to look further. He directs his assistant to pull the raw data on animal testing from Pharmacom's archives. He finds that several of the dogs that were tested experienced transient periods of heightened levels of blood pressure during the time that they were monitored. These findings did not appear in the summary figures reported to federal regulatory agencies, or in the quarterly reports produced by Pharmacom. Bob requests the autopsy report on the dead dog. He finds that the researchers had been surprised to discover that the dog had been pregnant.

Bob is startled at the information he has accidentally uncovered. He knows that Artharex is not marketed for use in pregnant women, but he also knows from his experience as a clinician that the drug is sometimes prescribed to reduce the aches and pains associated with weight gain in pregnancy. Bob knows how difficult it is to extrapolate from a small animal sample a potential risk calculation to pregnant women. He calls in his chief of biostatistics, who refuses to make a determination on the basis of such a small sample.

Bob takes the information to John Deal, Pharmacom's executive vice president and the man who hired Bob. "I recommend that we report these data to the U.S. Food and Drug Administration immediately. We have had no report of problems yet, but lives are potentially at risk if we don't get this information to doctors," Bob says.

Deal is stunned. "Do you have any idea what you are saying? If we release this now, the news will be devastating to our plans for expansion. Our stock offering will sink, and the value of the company—based on our success with Artharex—will be questioned in the financial markets. We will have to cancel our plans for expansion and revoke our collaboration agreements. We won't have the cash we need to sustain the research we envision. I know how strapped the University Health Center is right now. Its future is, to a large extent, dependant on our collaboration."

Deal says thoughtfully, "Pharmacom's reputation depends on its integrity. We can't risk lives, but I don't think this is the case here. The drug has never been marketed for use in pregnant women, and we have no knowledge that its use has caused an injury or even a complication."

Bob nods his agreement.

Deal continues, "The executive committee meets next month. The president of the center will be attending. Clear your calendar so that you can be there. We will make this a priority at the meeting. You set up the research protocols we will need to demonstrate conclusively a finding way one or another. But I believe that we should hold off any announcement of this concern until the stock offering is complete. It is only a matter of days."

39

A Nurse's Dilemma

Susan E. Kennel

Mr. P is a sixty-six-year-old, recently retired steel mill worker. His wife, a sixty-four-year-old homemaker, is in reasonably good health. He has four grown children who live nearby and are close to their father. Two years ago, Mr. P was diagnosed with advanced prostate cancer after experiencing difficulty with urination. He has had surgery and more recently chemotherapy, which provided him with temporary relief. Mr. P is now complaining of back pain that is not relieved using over-the-counter pain medications.

Mr. P's oncologist has recommended that he participate in a Phase I clinical trial to test a new medication that may be useful in the treatment of advanced prostate cancer.[1] His doctor has explained the trial procedures to Mr. P and his wife. They both read the consent form but have some difficulty understanding the terminology. Mr. P signs the form without any further questions, because he believes that his physician would not recommend a treatment that was not in his best interest.

Nurse A has worked in the oncology clinic for five years and has developed good working relationships with the clinic's oncologists. There are times, however, when she feels that they are overly aggressive and optimistic in their eagerness to enroll patients into their research trials. She has developed a close relationship with Mr. P and his wife over the course of his two years of treatment, and has been his primary nurse in the clinic. Nurse A knows that this new medication that has been recommended to Mr. P is very toxic and that the chances it will prove to be beneficial are slim. During one of his clinic visits, Mr. P begins talking to Nurse A about how fortunate he feels to be included in this trial. He asks her when she thinks he will start to feel better, because he and his wife would like to make vacation plans.

It is clear to Nurse A that Mr. P does not understand the purpose of the trial or the expected effects of this new medication. She is not comfortable providing any additional information without first speaking to the physician. Mr. P, sensing her hesitation, becomes anxious and begins to ask more pointed questions. "This medicine is going to help my pain, isn't it?"

Nurse A voices her concerns to the physician, who tells her that he spent a "lot of time" explaining the purpose of the research study to Mr. P and his wife and that he has fulfilled his ethical and legal obligations. He assures the nurse that no coercion was involved and that participating in this research study is the only chance Mr. P has for even minimal extension of his life. He gives Nurse A a copy of "Research Permission Guidelines," developed by the sponsoring hospital's institutional review board. One of the guidelines states that the research subject "should be given adequate information so that a reasonable person would understand the purpose, risks, and possible benefits from the research."

NOTES

1. A Phase I trial of an experimental drug typically assesses the drug's safety for humans, not its efficacy; that is, the efficacy of a drug in Phase I trials has not been established. Efficacy is typically investigated in Phase II trials.

40

A Researcher's Dilemma

Edward M. Spencer

High-Tech Hospital (HTH) is a modern, 350-bed flagship facility of a healthcare system that also includes several smaller hospitals and three nursing homes. HTH has an excellent staff, a small number of whom participate in research (mainly anti-cancer drug trials). Research is not considered a primary function of HTH, and most of the patients who come to the hospital are not aware that research is being conducted there.

One of the oncologists associated with the hospital is particularly interested in research and is a participant researcher in a number of clinical trials. Because of his busy oncology practice and his significant involvement in oncology drug trials, many of his patients have become involved in the drug trials he is sponsoring at HTH. The institutional review board (IRB) at HTH has questioned this apparent "conflict of interest" on a few occasions, but has been satisfied by the physician's statement that he will always put the interests of his patients first.

The oncologist is presently involved in a multiple-center drug trial. The drug is being studied in a double-blind fashion (that is, neither the researcher nor the patient knows whether the patient is receiving the drug or a placebo) as a potential treatment for metastatic melanoma. The oncologist recently attended a meeting where he heard rumors that this drug was showing significant positive results in a similar study begun in England, but that these results were not yet ready to be published. This rumor was verified in a conversation with an oncologist from England, who had been a researcher in the trial. There were also rumors that the study of the drug was soon to be "unblinded" (that is, investigators would disclose who was receiving the drug and who was receiving the placebo) with a recommendation that all patients receive the drug because of the early positive results in the study.

On the day after his return from the meeting, the oncologist sees a long-term patient with metastatic melanoma who is doing very poorly and is near death. This patient has been enrolled in the drug study and has received no benefit from the study. The physician believes that the patient is receiving the placebo and therefore has no chance of benefit from the drug trial. If the rumor is true that the drug is benefiting those who are taking it, then the drug represents this patient's only chance for a greater length and quality of life. The oncologist has several samples of the drug on hand that he could give to this patient after stopping the drug protocol. The oncologist wonders where his responsibility lies.

41

A Strategic Alliance

Ann E. Mills

The board of a large nonprofit medical center meets to discuss the possibility of forming an affiliated for-profit research center. The plan hinges on a three-way alliance between the medical school and its faculty, a newly created research center, and several pharmaceutical and biotechnology companies. The companies would provide the funds for research on projects that stand a chance of producing profits within a few years, and the medical center would provide the faculty to carry out the research.

Mr. N, a large and energetic man of around fifty is presenting the proposal. He begins, "Let's talk through the concept before we get to the details. Your medical center is being squeezed by shortfalls caused by the Balanced Budget Act of 1997 and declining reimbursement rates from the managed-care organizations that contract with you. Coupled with this scenario is the fact that a large portion of your patient population is indigent, and you don't begin to recover indigent care expenses from the state. So you are faced with the same sort of problems facing many others medical centers. You can't fund your research mission through cost shifting, as you have been able to do in the past. Almost 80 percent of your research funding comes from the National Insitutes of Health, but the NIH has certain restrictions that prevent you and your faculty from benefiting from your own research."

Mr. N takes a sip of water and glances at his notes before continuing, "The difference between you and other medical centers of your size is your superb faculty and your location, which is central to three urban centers and allows you a large patient population pool from which to draw research subjects. But your faculty is paid, on average, 12 percent less than others at comparable medical centers. This is your competitive advantage, and you are going to lose it, given the opportunities that exist for scientific and research personnel in the private sector and at other similar establishments."

The chairman of the board nods, "We know this. We have considered relaxing some of our conflict-of-interest policies for just that reason. What is your suggestion?"

Mr. N looks around at the fifteen well-dressed men and women sitting at the large, round table that dominates the oak-paneled room. "A for-profit research center funded by us and staffed by you. A joint venture means that we can develop our projects faster, which means that we can get them to market faster. An equitable profit-sharing arrangement would allow the medical center to adjust your faculty's salaries upward and intensify your recruitment efforts. In addition, revenue from patents would be shared. This would allow you more control over your future."

The medical center's chief executive officer (CEO) asks, "How would we structure such an agreement? It sounds fine in principle, but academic research centers have more than just one agenda. For instance, one reason we have been able to keep our faculty is our commitment to academic freedom. Presumably, you and the consortium you represent would want some say about publishing the results of the research."

The CEO clears his throat and continues, "I also understand that the state's attorney general has shown some interest in your consortium. There has been some talk of fraud—some concern that your consortium has misrepresented the efficacy of some of your products."

Mr. N nods. "Let me take your points one at a time," he replies. "The matter you are referring to is a dead issue. The state does not have the evidence to proceed against us, and we have already agreed to pay a fine and change our marketing tactics."

Mr. N drums his fingers impatiently, "There is a lot happening in the research world. You don't want to take a chance of not contributing to it or benefiting from it. We can work out details like when and how much to publish, which are relatively minor, on a project-by-project basis. No one is going to force anyone to do anything they don't want to do. Those who don't want to work in the research center aren't going to be forced to join our team. But I think you will find that your faculty will be amenable to our suggestions if they come attractively packaged. The point is to agree in principle, and then we can get the lawyers moving. Being associated with a for-profit is the engine you need to propel you through the next century."

42

Off-Site Patient Research

Patricia H. Werhane

A meeting is being held in the conference room in a large academic healthcare organization (HCO) that is located in the Midwest—an area that has suffered from excess bed supply for several years. Hospitals in this area have faced serious community resistance that has prevented them from significant downsizing or closures. Prevented from cost shifting by declining revenues from patient care activities, the academic HCO is seeking to generate more research funding from private sources rather than from the National Institutes of Health (NIH).

The meeting is between Jack Jensen, Bert Mansfield, Gene Smithson, and Sandra Alderman, MD, a senior administrator in the academic HCO. All four are concerned about delays in a research project that are associated with the organization's institutional review board (IRB). Specifically, the IRB has refused to approve the project under discussion because of its concerns with the patient recruitment strategy outlined in the proposal.

Jack Jensen represents a large pharmaceutical company that is interested in cosponsoring the research study, which would be managed and conducted by the HCO. Bert Mansfield represents WellCare, the other cosponsor. WellCare is a large health-maintenance organization that uses the academic HCO for many of its inpatients. This patient base contributes 25 percent of the HCO's revenues from patient care activities. Gene Smithson is the senior vice president of business development at Total Clinical Research, a full-service contract research organization and study site that supports a dedicated IRB.

Jensen opens the conversation. "Your IRB has not approved the study we outlined for you several months ago." He shakes his head. "The principal investigator and his research team are excited about developing this project. We are looking at appropriate medication for asthma in children. You know how beneficial this could be for children of all ages."

Dr. Alderman responds. "The IRB is concerned about your recruitment methods. I understand that your company and WellCare intend to use patient records generated through visits here to identify research subjects. The IRB is concerned that identifying subjects in this manner is unethical and may violate our policies on patient confidentiality and privacy."

Mr. Smithson interjects, "Mr. Jensen and Mr. Mansfield have shared your organization's concerns with me and have invited my participation at this meeting. They suggest changing the patient recruitment strategy as your IRB suggests. My company, Total Clinical Research, will have responsibility for all recruitment efforts. Our company has a large database of primary-care physicians whom we contact regularly about proposed studies. Obviously, we have access to primary-care physicians who are associated with WellCare, but we also have access to physicians who are associated with WellCare's competitors. We spend a lot of time developing relationships with all of our docs. We ask them to secure permission from patients—or their legal guardians—so we can contact them about proposed clinical trials that may be of interest to them. Once we have permission, we collect personal information on proposed subjects to match them with appropriate clinical trials. But we have a strict privacy policy. This is our role—to match patients with appropriate clinical trials."

Mr. Mansfield leans forward and smiles. "We believe that this should address your IRB's concerns. Our organization will delegate responsibility for recruitment to Total Clinical Research. But we have another suggestion to make that we hope you will consider. Total Clinical Research supports a dedicated IRB. We want to use their IRB on this project. Your IRB is overburdened as it is. They only meet every few weeks, so they don't have time to appropriately monitor a sensitive project like this. The IRB members associated with Total Clinical Research are fully conversant with U.S. Food and Drug Administration and National Institutes of Health mandates. We asked them to look at the changed proposal. They were happy with it and have said that they would be glad to serve as the monitoring device for the project. A person who is attached to their IRB will be assigned as a full-time manager to the project and will coordinate activities with the principal investigator of the project."

Mr. Mansfield leans back in his chair and continues, "Subcontracting this responsibility to Total Clinical Research will relieve your IRB. It will move the project forward, and it will relieve any tension between your organization and mine. After all, we are a large customer of yours, and your competitor is only a few miles down the road."

43

The Recalcitrant Drug Trial

Sue McCoy

Dr. Mason is a very popular pulmonologist who teaches at the medical school affiliated with a large metropolitan hospital. He has a large contract with a drug company to randomize his patients with pneumonia, who receive either a new antibiotic, Killsall, or a second-generation cephalosporin. Killsall has been shown to be superior in animal studies and in preliminary trials in humans, because it not only eliminates more types of bacteria but also has fewer side-effects.

Senior managers in the hospital are particularly pleased with the project, because the drug company pays the hospital very generously for its part in the drug trial. Mr. Newnan, a contract specialist and senior administrator for the hospital, is reviewing the contract with Dr. Mason. Both men believe the contract is fair. It allows Dr. Mason to publish his results, and Dr. Mason is due to apply for promotion and tenure soon and needs a solid publication to strengthen his application. It also gives him a tidy nest egg to support other research he is planning. The contract also implies that if the results of the test are favorable to Killsall, the company will plan other trials. Mr. Newnan believes that the preliminary research is sound; that the trial will support the use of Killsall; and, thus, that other studies will follow. The drug company is known to be generous to its partners in research.

After the first 200 patients have been randomized and treated with Killsall or the control drug, the code is broken and Dr. Mason and the company scrutinize the data. They find that, so far, Killsall has slightly less antibacterial activity and at least as many side-effects as the control drug. However, not enough patients have participated in the study to reach statistical significance. The drug company wants to quell publication and threatens to move the study to another hospital with the hope of more positive results. Dr. Mason thinks it is very important that the study results be published now. He says microbiologists and infectious disease specialists should know about the results to date.

Mr. Newnan is uncertain how to proceed. He wonders if Dr. Mason is thinking of his promotion and tenure application, and he is concerned about the potential loss of current and projected revenue to the hospital.

44

The Olivieri/Apotex Affair

Ann E. Mills

Below is a brief outline of a story that consumed the international medical and academic community for more than five years.[1] The case remains controversial.

BACKGROUND

Clinical trials of the drug deferiprone were conducted at the Hospital for Sick Children in Toronto from 1989 to 1997. The Hospital for Sick children is one of the teaching and research hospitals affiliated with the University of Toronto. The hospital and the university collaborate on teaching and research activities as well as on seeking innovative ways to improve the health of children. The patients involved in this drug trial were children and young adults suffering from thalassemia major, a serious and potentially fatal disease. Deferiprone (L1) was a newly developed compound for ameliorating the serious side-effects of the only known treatment for the severe anemia manifested by patients with the disease. The principal investigators

---

Although the events in this case occurred in Canada, the U.S. and Canada follow similar drug-testing procedures. The clinical testing of experimental drugs is typically done in three phases; each successive phase involves a larger number of subjects. Phase I studies are primarily concerned with assessing a drug's safety. They are designed to determine what happens to the drug in the human body; how it is absorbed, metabolized, excreted. Phase I studies investigate side-effects that occur as dosage levels are increased. Once a drug has been tested for safety, it is tested for efficacy in a Phase II trial. This second phase typically lasts longer and involves more patients than Phase I trials. In Phase III studies, a drug is tested in several hundred to several thousand patients; most Phase III studies are randomized and blinded trials that usually last several years. Phase IV trials are follow-up studies conducted after a drug is allowed on the market.

included Nancy Olivieri, MD, and Gideon Koren, MD, members of the hospital's clinical and research staff. The sponsors were the Medical Research Council of Canada (MCR)—the major federal research agency funding health sciences research in Canada and the country's largest single funder of such research—and Apotex, Inc.—a major producer of generic drugs.[2]

Olivieri's interest in deferiprone was its potential to help treat thalassemia, a genetic disorder that results in severe anemia. The only available treatment for this disease is monthly transfusions of red blood cells, which causes life-threatening complications: the iron from the red blood cells accumulates in the body, damaging the heart and liver. To get rid of the iron, patients are hooked up to a battery-operated pump that slowly injects the drug deferoxamine for a twelve-hour period, four to six days a week. The new drug, deferiprone, could be administered in pill form, eliminating the often unbearable standard treatment.[3]

HISTORY

In 1995, Olivieri and her colleagues published the results of a three-year Phase II trial (a "compassionate-use" trial) of L1 on twenty-one patients who were unable or unwilling to follow the standard therapy.[4] They reported a steady decline in iron levels in the study group. The trial had been funded by the MRC beginning in July 1989. The protocol under which the trial was conducted came to be known as LA-03. It was the data from this protocol that caused the ensuing controversy: Olivieri's results showed a steady decline in iron levels in her study group.

In 1991, MRC suggested that Olivieri secure private funding for a larger randomized trial (a Phase III trial) in which L1 would be compared with deferoxamine, the standard treatment. Olivieri and Koren approached Michael Spino, MD, vice president for scientific affairs at Apotex, with general responsibility for the development of new compounds. Before he joined Apotex in 1992, Spino had held a full-time appointment in the Faculty of Pharmacy of the University of Toronto and an appointment in the Hospital for Sick Children's Division of Clinical Pharmacology and Toxicology. After joining Apotex, he resigned his university position and was appointed to a full professor "status-only" position; he was not paid by the university, but he was, however, allowed to retain laboratory and office space at the university and hospital in order to conduct research and supervise graduate students and fellows. Koren and Spino had collaborated on a variety of projects before the deferiprone study.[5]

On 2 April 1993, Olivieri and Koren entered into a three-year clinical trials contract with Apotex. The contract outlined the responsibilities of the investigators and the sponsor. Apotex would provide the drug and fund the study, and the investigators would perform Phase III clinical studies on L1. In addition, the contained the following clause pertaining to confidentiality:

> All information, whether written or not, obtained or generated by the investigators during the term of this agreement and for a period of one year thereafter, shall be and remain secret and confidential and shall not be disclosed in any manner to any third party, except to an appropriate regulatory agency for the purpose of obtaining regulatory approval to manufacture, use or sell L1, unless the information has been previously disclosed to the public with the consent of Apotex. The investigators shall not submit any information for publication without the prior written approval of Apotex.[6]

Although hospital policy required the hospital's research ethics board (REB) to approve the study protocol, there was no hospital policy that clearly required review and approval of contracts in advance. Olivieri and Koren did not submit the trials contract to the hospital's REB for review or approval before its execution.[7]

The research protocol for the clinical trials (LA-01 protocol), prepared and signed by Apotex and the investigators, was submitted to the hospital's REB for approval. The protocol described the procedures for conducting the randomized trials, information to be provided to patients about risks and benefits of participating in the trials, informed consent, monitoring, safety measures, stopping rules, and requirements for reporting unexpected findings and adverse reactions. The protocol also contained provisions pertaining to confidentiality of information and publication rights that differed from provisions on these topics contained in the trials contract. The hospital's REB approved the research protocols.[8] The LA-01 protocol included Geoffrey Dougherty, MD, as an investigator, in addition to Olivieri and Koren. The study design involved enrolling 33 patients in each arm of the trial. Because Olivieri was unable to enroll enough patients at the Toronto sites, additional patients were enrolled at the Montreal Children's Hospital under Dougherty's supervision.

Because the study was small and because of the limited market potential of L1 in Canada, Apotex agreed in 1994 to complement the Canadian study with a larger international trial in centers in the United States and Italy (LA-02 protocol). The investigators in the trial agreed to the establishment of a steering committee, and Olivieri agreed to serve as chair of the committee and consultant for the project. A contract was executed between Olivieri and Apotex on 17 June 1995 retroactive to

October 1994, in which she received a retainer, \$U.S. 30,000 per year, plus \$U.S. 200 per diem during travel, and out-of-pocket travel expenses. Olivieri did not submit the contract for hospital approval. It contained intellectual property provisions, publication provisions, and the following confidentiality provision:

> All information, whether written or not, obtained or generated by "The Consultant" during the term of this contract, and for a period of three (3) years thereafter, shall be and remain secret and confidential and shall not be disclosed in any manner, whatsoever to any third party, except to an appropriate regulatory agency for the purpose of obtaining regulatory approval for manufacture, use or sale of "deferiprone" unless the information has been previously disclosed to the public with the consent of "Apotex."[9]

CONFLICT

Shortly after the publication of the April 1995 article about the promising results of the Phase II trial (LA-03 trial) in the *New England Journal of Medicine,* Olivieri began to have concerns about patients' response to L1, as there appeared to be a loss of efficacy of the drug in a significant number of subjects. Apotex did not share this view, and, by February 1996, it became clear that there were serious disagreements between Apotex and the investigators about the interpretation of the data on the efficacy of L1.[10] Olivieri forwarded to Spino the text of a report she intended to send the REB on the "loss of efficacy" of the drug. Spino responded by indicating that Apotex needed and was entitled to all the raw data from the original LA-03 trial, which Olivieri and Koren had initiated long before Apotex became involved.

In March 1996, Olivieri submitted a report titled "Variability in Therapeutic Response to Deferiprone" to Stanley Zlotkin, MD, PhD, chair of the hospital's REB, in which she expressed her misgivings about the efficacy of the drug. That same month, Spino sent a document to Zlotkin describing the "Apotex view" and disputing Olivieri's findings.[11]

In April 1996, Zlotkin, on behalf of the hospital's REB, advised Olivieri to do the following: (1) change information and consent forms, (2) report her findings to appropriate regulatory bodies, (3) report her findings to the physicians responsible for the care of patients and the ethics committees at the hospitals where the patients received care, (4) evaluate the continued efficacy of the drug if the trial were to continue, (5) submit a separate protocol demonstrating how that would be done, and (6) ensure that appropriate diagnostic measures were in place to evaluate the continued efficacy of L1 in patients receiving the drug under the LA-01 protocol. In addition, Zlotkin advised Olivieri that, with respect to the LA-02 trial in the United States and Italy, Olivieri could not participate in a study involving human subjects (even though the trial was taking place outside of the hospital) unless its protocol had been reviewed and approved by the hospital's REB.

In May 1996, Spino wrote to Zlotkin commenting on these instructions and informing Zlotkin that all of the investigators had been provided with Olivieri's report and Apotex's rebuttal, and that all of them had indicated that the data did not warrant notification of their respective REBs. Spino also stated that Apotex had convened an expert advisory panel of international stature to evaluate the data.[12]

On 24 May 1996, Spino wrote to Olivieri and Koren indicating that their contract with Apotex had expired and would not be extended or renewed, and that the LA-01 and LA-03 trials would be discontinued at the Hospital for Sick Children and the Toronto Hospital. He concluded the letter with the following paragraph:

> As you know, paragraph 7 of the LA-01 Agreement and the LA-01 and LA-03 Protocols provide that all information, whether written or not, obtained or generated by the Investigators during the term of the LA-01 Agreement and for a period of one year thereafter, shall be and remain secret and confidential and shall not be disclosed in any manner to any third party except with the prior written consent of Apotex. Please be aware that Apotex will take all possible steps to ensure that these obligations of confidentiality are met and will vigorously pursue all legal remedies in the event there is any breach of these obligations.[13]

On the same date, Spino notified Olivieri of termination of Olivieri's consulting contract with Apotex for services related to the LA-02 trial. The concluding paragraph of his letter stated:

> As you know, paragraph 7 of the LA-02 Contract provides that all information, whether written or not, obtained or generated by the Investigators during the term of the LA-02 Contract and for a period of three years thereafter, shall be and remain secret and confidential and shall not be disclosed in any manner to any third party except with the prior written consent of Apotex. Please be aware that Apotex will take all possible steps to ensure that these obligations of confidentiality are met and will vigorously pursue all legal remedies in the event there is any breach of these obligations.[14]

THE LEGAL PREDICAMENT

The secretary-treasurer of the Canadian Medical Protective Association described Olivieri's legal predicament as follows:

> You have become persuaded that you are in possession of important information which, for the sake of persons throughout the world, you as a research scientist have an obligation to disclose to regulatory officials and to the scientific community. At the same time, you remain bound by the terms of your contract with Apotex to disclose information arising from your research only as you have the permission of Apotex to do so. . . . You are [also] rightly concerned that failure on your part to make any reasonable disclosure at all of the conclusions you have reached may put you in jeopardy of legal action by persons who will allege that you have failed in your duty to protect them.[15]

THE HOSPITAL'S RESPONSE

Olivieri contacted hospital authorities the day after she received notice that her contract with Apotex would not be extended or renewed. In her letter to senior medical and administrative personnel, she wrote:

> Because this series of events has ethical implications for the safety of patients, both those in whom loss of efficacy has been observed, and all of those who, in good faith, signed a consent and information form to complete this trial at The Hospital for Sick Children, as well as to the Hospital itself and to ourselves as researchers, we will need your advice and guidance as to how to proceed.[16]

Hospital authorities were able to negotiate two substantive issues between Olivieri and Apotex—the appropriate cessation of the L1 clinical trial and agreement to report the information to Health Canada's Health Protection Branch (the regulatory body that establishes standards for clinical trials of new drugs). No other advice or active support (moral or otherwise) seemed to be forthcoming from the hospital at that time, other than a meeting arranged by Arnold Aberman (dean of the University of Toronto Faculty of Medicine) between himself and Jack Kay, a senior executive with Apotex. Aberman recalls the meeting as follows:

> I had never met him before (or since). I knew his name because a friend of mine is a lawyer who acts, from time to time, on tax matters only, for Apotex. We met at the Prince Hotel coffee shop. At the meeting I advised him that, irrespective of rights that Apotex may

believe it has, Apotex should stop threatening legal action against Nancy [Olivieri] and should not proceed with legal action. The meeting was cordial and Mr. Kay said that he would consider my request.[17]

By this point, Olivieri had secured the services of a lawyer.

CONSEQUENCES

Olivieri continued to insist that she be allowed to publish or present her observations of the trials, and Apotex continued to resist. Spino said that the company did not want to suppress information but it did want to prevent Olivieri from promulgating misinformation.[18] Apotex continued to press the issue of breach of contract. In November 1996, Spino wrote to Olivieri:

In these circumstances, and after reviewing the matter with legal counsel, Apotex has no alternative but to advise that you are no longer a member of the LA-02 Steering Committee and will accordingly not be invited to future LA-02 Steering Committee meetings. [Olivieri no longer had a consulting contract for the international trials, but she had remained a member of the steering committee as specified in the LA-02 protocols that formed the basis of regulatory approval for the trial.]

Please note that you are not entitled to obtain further information pertaining to data or results regarding Apotex-sponsored studies from any of the investigators without the prior written approval of Apotex. Furthermore, may I remind you that any information pertaining to Apotex-sponsored studies which you may have obtained, whether from Apotex or others, remains confidential proprietary information of Apotex.[19]

The hospital appeared to maintain a neutral stance in the dispute. A Toronto newspaper reported that, when questioned about the hospital's role, Aberman said that the issue involved a scientific dispute and therefore he did not need to take sides.[20]

On 24 September 1997, Anne Marie Christian, associate director (administration) of the Research Institute (the hospital's research division) consulted Borden & Elliot, the hospital's legal counsel, with respect to the enforceability of the confidentiality clause in the Apotex-Olivieri-Koren agreement, the overriding responsibilities of a physician who believes that a drug being tested in a clinical trial causes harm to patients, and the position the hospital should take if Apotex threatened legal action. On 23 October 1997, the legal firm indicated that, depending on the specific facts in the case, the confidentiality clause in the agreement was "probably enforceable." The lawyers declined to comment on the physician's disclosure responsibilities because the firm of Borden & Elliot did not represent Olivieri. Given that the hospital was not party to the Apotex agreement, counsel did not think that the hospital needed to take a position in the dispute and probably should not do so.[21]

AFTERWORD

By January 1997 the media had become aware of the increasingly bitter situation at the hospital. In August 1998 Olivieri said that the hospital tried to fire her twice,[22] and there were reports of threats and intimidation against those who supported her.[23] In September 1998, after 140 doctors signed a petition demanding an external inquiry into the dispute and after top scientists at the hospital threatened to take their research elsewhere,[24] hospital board members voted for an independent probe into the affair.[25] The board announced that it had retained Arnold Naimark, MD, a respected medical doctor, scientist, educator, and head of the University of Manitoba's Center for Advancement of Medicine, to conduct the investigation.

Initially, Olivieri and her supporters welcomed the announcement, but they later expressed concern that the report would be biased. The Canadian Association of University Teachers issued a statement, adopted unanimously at its annual general meeting, calling for a full and independent inquiry into the dispute and asking that any report produced by Naimark be shelved. They alleged that Naimark, as former president of the University of Manitoba, had a previous relationship with Apotex. Specifically, they said that the company donated $120,000 to the institution.[26] Olivieri, fearing bias, refused to take part in the report.

Others expressed concern about the appearance of an institutional conflict of interest at both the university and the hospital. Barry Sherman, the head of Apotex, was also head of one of Canada's largest private charitable bodies, the Apotex Foundation. At the University of Toronto, the potential conflict involved the university's negotiations with the Apotex Foundation for a substantial donation that would help the medical school expand its facilities. Sue Bloch-Nevitte, director of communications for the university's fund-raising campaign, reported that the university hoped "that the Shermans would consider making a sizeable donation upwards of perhaps $20 million to the facility."[27] At the hospital, the potential conflict involved a possible donation of $10 million from the Apotex Foundation. Dianne Lister, president of the Hospital for Sick Children's Foundation, confirmed that the Apotex

Foundation had offered the money to one of the city's teaching hospitals; the funds would accompany the foundation's expected donation to the medical school.[28]

On 12 August 1998, the day the *New England Journal of Medicine* published Olivieri's article questioning the long-term safety and effectiveness of L1,[29] Mike Strofolino, president of the Hospital for Sick Children, announced that the hospital had declined the $10 million donation from the Apotex Foundation.[30]

NOTES

1. This case presentation quotes extensively from the "Naimark Report"—a report published under the auspices of the Hospital for Sick Children—which is controversial because Olivieri refused to participate in the review. It remains posted on the hospital's website as the official report of the dispute that involved Olivieri, her colleagues at the hospital, and members of the international medical and scientific community. It is titled *L1 Clinical Trials Review* and is available at <http://www.sickkids.on.ca/l1trials/revcontents.asp >.

2. <http://www.sickkids.on.ca/l1trials/introduction.as >.

3. Canadian Association of University Teachers, *Bulletin Online* 45, no. 7 (September 1998). Available at < http://www.caut.ca/English/bulletin/98_spet/lead.htm>.

4. N. Olivieri et al., "Iron-Chelation Therapy with Oral Deferiprone in Patients with Thalassemia," *New England Journal of Medicine* 332, no. 14 (6 April 1995). Available at <http://www.nejm.org/content/1995/0332/0014/0918.asp 5>.

5. See note 2 above.

6. <http://www.sickkids.on.ca/l1trials/initiation.asp>.

7. Ibid.

8. Ibid.

9. Ibid.

10. <http://www.orsil.ubc.ca/Apotex.htm>. See also <http://www.sickkids.on.ca/l1trials/scientific.asp>.

11. <http://www.sickkids.on.ca/l1trials/ethics.asp>.

12. <http://www.sickkids.on.ca/l1trials/nonrenewel.asp>.

13. <http://www.sickkids.on.ca/l1trials/involvement.asp>.

14. Ibid.

15. Ibid.

16. <http://www.sickkids.on.ca/l1trials/consequences.asp>.

17. See note 13 above.

18. M. Shuchman, "Potential for Conflicts in Drug Research Medical Research Ethics," *Toronto Star,* 27 October 1998, A20.

19. <http://www.sickkids.on.ca/l1trials/consequences.asp>.

20. See note 18 above.

21. <http://www.sickkids.on.ca/l1trials/question.asp>.

22. See note 18 above.

23. R. Daly, "Scientists Up Ante in Sick Kids Fight: Researchers Threaten to

Leave if Demand for Inquiry Isn't Met," *Toronto Star,* 28 August 1998, B4.

24. Ibid.

25. S. Lem, "Hospital OKs Probe in Drug Test Furor," *Toronto Star,* 10 September 1998, 38.

26. R. Daly, "Sick Kids' Researcher Gets Support Faculty Calls for Unbiased Review of Drug Dispute," *Toronto Star,* 25 November 1998, A2.

27. See note 18 above.

28. Ibid.

29. N. Olivieri et al., "Long-Term Safety and Effectiveness of Iron-Chelation Therapy with Deferiprone for Thalassemia Major," *New England Journal of Medicine* 339, no. 7 (13 August 1998). Available at <http://www.nejm.org/content/1998/0339/0007/0417.asp>.

30. See note 18 above.

Appendixes

Appendix A

Virginia Bioethics Network Recommendations for Guidelines on Procedures and Process to Address Organization Ethics in Healthcare Organizations

Edward M. Spencer

BACKGROUND

In 1995 the Virginia Bioethics Network (VBN) adopted "Recommendations and Guidelines for Procedures and Process and Education and Training to Strengthen Bioethics Services in Virginia" (hereafter, the Recommendations). This set of guidelines focused on helping healthcare organizations (HCOs) respond to the needs for ethics services within the organization and surrounding community. The VBN also anticipated that the Recommendations could be used as a tool for HCOs to evaluate their ethics services and direct them toward appropriate decisions for improvement of these services. The Recommendations also defined certain educational requirements for ethics committee members, ethics consultants, and teachers of introductory and advanced clinical ethics courses.

Since the VBN's action, a number of HCOs, both within Virginia and in other states, have used the Recommendations to strengthen and evaluate their individual ethics programs. Many of these HCOs have reported that the Recommendations have been valuable in preparing for Joint Commission on Accreditation of Healthcare Organizations (JCAHO) inspections and in addressing issues during the inspections. This positive aspect of the recommendations was not unexpected, as consultation with Paul Schyve, Senior Vice President, JCAHO, continued throughout their development.

INTRODUCTION

In 1995 JCAHO added a section called "Organization Ethics" to its section, Patient Rights. This was accomplished without fanfare and with very little notice from the community of HCOs that JCAHO accredits. This change, however, has far-reaching implications for the future operations of HCOs and their internal and external relationships (including relationships with healthcare professionals and managed care organizations). Depending on interpretation and implementation, these new Standards could well become the framework for assuring ethical oversight of the ever-changing healthcare arena for the foreseeable future.

Dr. Schyve has publicly stated on a number of occasions that he believes that the ethics committee in each HCO should be the organizational base for attention to organization ethics. He has challenged the administrations of HCOs to use their ethics committees in this manner and has at the same time challenged ethics committees to rethink and expand their traditional role and services and to make necessary changes to respond to this new and important area.

Ethics committees have responded to this challenge in one of two ways: (1) beginning the process of reorganization required by this new mandate by considering the issues of "organization ethics" and developing a strategy to respond, or (2) refusing to become involved at all in organization ethics or asking to be involved only peripherally. VBN believes that the first response is the appropriate one, since it assures that the ethics committee will continue to be a leader in developing and overseeing ethics services within the HCO. This position also assures the HCO board and administration that ethical issues associated with organization ethics will be addressed in an open manner by a committed multi-disciplinary group with input from community members, and that ethics processes, which lead to the best in patient care, which assure professional integrity of the practicing clinicians, and which assure that the HCO maintains the highest of ethical standards in its business and management activities, will be developed and maintained.

VBN's Board of Directors, in its annual meeting in October 1996, voted to develop new guidelines addressing the appropriate response of a HCO's ethics committee to organization ethics issues similar to the recommendations which address the more traditional activities of ethics committees.

The following guidelines have been developed with consultation and input from VBN members and the staff at the University of Virginia's (UVa's) Center for Biomedical Ethics. The guidelines have been revised after input from each of these groups and the final version has been approved by the VBN Board. These new "guidelines" are only recommendations and are meant to be adopted or rejected piecemeal or in toto by the boards of HCOs. VBN does not claim that these "guidelines" represent the only or even the best way to respond to the issues of organization ethics. They do, however, represent thoughtful consideration of these issues by VBN member institutions, VBN individual members, and staff members at the UVa Center for Biomedical Ethics, with the goal of helping to develop a workable mechanism to address organization ethics issues in each HCO, thereby assuring ethics oversight of the policies and processes affecting the organizational aspects of the HCO.

DEFINITION

"Organization ethics" consists of a process(es) to address ethical issues associated with the business, financial, and management areas of healthcare organizations, as well as with professional, educational, and contractual relationships affecting the operation of the HCO.

GUIDELINE 1

Organization ethics shall be addressed by each HCO's ethics program. VBN believes that the ethics committee is the appropriate body within a HCO to address organization ethics issues for the following reasons.

1. Who better? There is no other established body within healthcare organizations that is as well prepared to address ethical issues in an open, honest, straightforward manner.
2. By accepting the responsibility for consideration of organization ethics issues, the ethics committee continues as the recognized source for ethics education, consultation, and policy review within the HCO.
3. Although expanding the committee's knowledge base to include the organization ethics arena may be necessary, the process remains essentially the same as that used for consideration of patient care ethics issues.
4. The ethics committee is less likely to be unduly influenced by business, financial, and legal considerations than a group composed of administrators, and/or financial officers, and/or institutional attorneys.
5. Attention to ethical issues in organization ethics is more likely to be accepted by an institution's patients and the community it serves if it is overseen by the ethics committee.

GUIDELINE 2

Reorganization of an organization's ethics committee and additional training of ethics committee members shall be undertaken by each HCO so that the ethics program can appropriately respond to organization ethics issues. If organization ethics is to be fully understood by the ethics committee so that it can be fair, objective, and efficient in addressing organization ethics issues, there will, by necessity, need to be changes in the organization and activities of the ethics committee. Following are examples that comprise one workable mechanism for instituting needed changes. Other mechanisms may work as well or better in particular HCOs.

1. Re-evaluate the ethics committee's mission statement, policies, and by-laws and change as needed to reflect the expanded scope and activities of the committee in addressing organization ethics issues.

2. Reorganize the ethics committee to include representatives from the business, finance, and management areas of the HCO.

    A. Enlarge committee and expand work to include organization ethics.

    B. Divide the committee into two subcommittees: "Patient Care" and "Organization Ethics." Each subcommittee would have primary responsibility for its particular set of issues, with the "Patient Care Subcommittee" being responsible for the patient care issues traditionally addressed by ethics committees, and the "Organization Ethics Subcommittee" being responsible for organization ethics issues. Both subcommittees should report to the full committee, and any actions or recommendations should be from the full ethics committee after appropriate consideration and discussion.

    VBN believes that dividing the committee into two focused subcommittees is the preferred mechanism for reorganization of the committee for most HCOs.

3. Begin the education program focused on organization ethics for committee members. Education should focus on (1) introducing ethics committee members to organization ethics; (2) increasing the committee's knowledge of the business, financial, and management aspects of the HCO including an introduction to particular ethical issues seen in these areas; (3) a study of conflicts of interest among healthcare professionals; and (4) theoretical and practical issues in "business ethics." This may require taking courses at local institutions of higher learning, taking short (one- or two-week) intensive courses focused on these issues, contracting with experts to develop and present required education, and discussion concerning these issues among all of the members of the newly formed ethics committee (with the new members from the business, management, and financial areas taking the lead in explaining the ethical principles they use in decision making).

GUIDELINE 3

The major functions of the organization ethics activities of the ethics committee shall be as follows: to develop or revise an organization code of ethics with attention to the organization's mission statement for guidance; to develop or revise policies that support the mission statement and the code of ethics; to develop an educational program concerning organization ethics issues for board members, clinicians, administrators, finance officers, and community members; and to institute a process for addressing issues and problems that arise in conjunction with organization ethics.

1. Develop or review the HCO's code of ethics. The JCAHO now requires that each HCO that it accredits have a code of ethics that addresses, at a minimum, the following issues: marketing, admission, transfer, discharge, billing practices, providers, payers, and educational institutions. To date, JCAHO has made few specific recommendations as to how the code should address each of these subjects. JCAHO does require that the code be consistent with the mission of the HCO and that, when needed, specific policies be developed to ensure that the code has meaning within the day-to-day operations of the HCO.

   An appropriate first task for the reorganized ethics committee should be review of the code (if one has been developed) with recommendations for change when needed, or the development of the code and supporting policies if this has not been done previously.

2. Develop and institute an educational program focused on organization ethics issues for the committee, the organization's staff (both clinical and nonclinical), and the community that the organization serves. The needed education can be accomplished in a number of ways, including lectures from outside experts, lectures from knowledgeable committee members and other staff members, panel discussions, general discussions led by a committee member, case discussions, and a repeatable course developed by the committee. Each committee will decide which of these educational programs are appropriate for the particular HCO. It is imperative for each ethics committee to begin its educational program as soon as possible and to obtain outside help when needed. (VBN will help its members and others with the development and presentation of educational sessions when needed.)

3. Ethics committees should recognize that certain problems and dilemmas related to organization ethics may occur, and a mechanism for addressing these organization ethics "cases" should be

developed. The mechanism chosen to address these cases can be similar to the patient care ethics consultation mechanism described in the Recommendations or may take some other form. Whatever approach is selected, a formal process defined by protocol should be developed and instituted to address the issues of access, notice, documentation, and evaluation of the process as well as education and training of those designated to be responsible for this process. (See Recommendations.)

GUIDELINE 4

The organization ethics aspect of the ethics committee shall develop one or more plans for coordination of attention to ethical issues based on the relationships between the HCO and (1) managed-care organizations with contractual association, (2) healthcare professionals, and (3) community organizations with ongoing relationships with the HCO.

Relationships and associations (professional, personal, and contractual) among those actively engaged in healthcare delivery are often of primary importance in understanding and resolving ethical problems. In spite of their importance, little attention has been directed toward these issues. VBN believes that the organization ethics activities of the ethics committee should include attention to these important aspects of the ethical climate of the organization.

1. It is appropriate for the ethics committee with an organization ethics function to consider how specific contractual obligations of the HCO do or do not correspond to the stated mission and code of ethics. The ethics committee should have no authority to change these contractual obligations but should be expected to call attention to perceived deviations from the mission and code within the organization.

2. It is appropriate for an ethics committee with an organization ethics function to offer assistance to healthcare professionals when problems occur based on conflicts between professional obligations and obligations imposed by administrative and regulatory structures. The ethics committee should not, however, be involved in strictly professional issues.

3. The ethics committee with an organization ethics function should recognize as part of its obligation enhancement of disclosure and communication between the HCO and (1) its employees, (2) its professional staff, (3) its contractual partners, and (4) most importantly, the community it serves.

Approved 25 October 1997.

Appendix B

A Framework for Case Analysis in Healthcare Organization Ethics

Ann E. Mills

IDENTIFY THE PROBLEM
1. What are the facts?
   A. What individual stakeholder or groups of stakeholders are affected?
   B. How are they affected?
   C. What systems, structures, or policies are affected?
   D. How are they affected?
2. What are the ethical issues involved from the perspective of individual stakeholders or groups of stakeholders?

OBTAIN BACKGROUND INFORMATION
1. What is the organization's mission?
2. What is the organization's vision?
3. What are the core values of organization?
4. Who are the organization's stakeholders?
5. What priority does the organization assign to each stakeholder or group of stakeholders?
6. How is that priority determined?

MAKE THE DECISION
1. Identify alternatives
2. Rank alternatives by asking:
   A. What is it that *can* be done within the context of the organization's mission, vision, and core values?
   B. What are anticipated outcomes from each alternative?

C. What impact will the decision have on individual stakeholders or groups of stakeholders?
  i.   Which individual stakeholder or stakeholder group ben-
       efits?
  ii. Which individual stakeholder or stakeholder group is
       harmed?
D. What impact will the decision have on the organization?
E. Will the decision have short-term or long-term effects on
the organization?

IMPLEMENT THE DECISION
1. Who is best person or group to implement the decision?
   A. Is there a conflict of interest in this choice? Can it be re-
      solved?
   B. Are accountability mechanisms in place?

MONITOR THE OUTCOMES
1. Are anticipated outcomes consistent with actual outcomes?

Appendix C

The Development of the Sentara Healthcare System's Ethics Program

Julia Milner West and Earl D. White, II

The following is a description of the development of an organization ethics program in a fully integrated healthcare system.

SENTARA HEALTHCARE

Sentara Healthcare is located in the Hampton Roads region of Virginia. Sentara is a local, not-for-profit healthcare system of nationally recognized, award-winning hospitals and healthcare facilities, renowned physicians, leading-edge services, and comprehensive health plans. It employs 12,000 individuals. In 1999, for the third year in a row, Hospitals and Health Networks named Sentara as one of the top ten most integrated healthcare organizations (HCOs) in the United States. Sentara's geographic reach is southeastern Virginia and northeastern North Carolina. It has five hospitals: Sentara Norfolk General Hospital, a 644-bed, tertiary-care facility located on a large medical campus including Eastern Virginia Medical School and the Children's Hospital of the Kings Daughters; Sentara Leigh Hospital; Sentara Bayside Hospital; Sentara Virginia Beach General Hospital; and Sentara Hampton General Hospital. In addition, it has an affiliation with Williamsburg Community Hospital, in Williamsburg, Virginia. Sentara is a self-contained HCO with its own home care, hospice, skilled nursing and long term-care facilities, mental health services, senior services, and health plans.[1]

SENTARA HEALTHCARE ETHICS: FIRST STEPS

In 1991 the Sentara Norfolk General Hospital's ethics committee invited persons known to be interested in healthcare ethics from across the organization to attend a meeting to study the most effective and least costly way to satisfy the newly introduced Virginia Natural Death Act. The Corporate Ethics Committee was formed at this meeting. In the next several years, this group deliberated only when necessary to keep abreast of changes in the law and to assess whether Sentara's processes fully reflected these changes.

SENTARA HEALTHCARE ETHICS ADVISORY COUNCIL

In 1995, the Joint Commission on Accreditation of Healthcare Organizations (JCAHO) initiated its first standards addressing "organization ethics," which is concerned with the ethical behavior of HCOs. The members of the Corporate Ethics Committee believed that JCAHO's new standards offered an opportunity for the committee to play a more proactive role in focusing attention on clinical ethics, professional ethics, and organization ethics within Sentara.

Sentara's administration provides financial support for educational opportunities that it believes are important to the development of new initiatives. The leadership of the Corporate Ethics Committee (and many members of ethics committees in each of Sentara's five hospitals) requested and received funds to attend, at various times, a week-long program called Developing Healthcare Ethics Programs (DHEP), an intensive program offered by the Center for Biomedical Ethics in the School of Medicine at the University of Virginia in Charlottesville. Several Sentara staff members also attended a week-long intensive program, Challenges in Contemporary Healthcare Ethics, offered by the Kennedy Institute of Ethics at Georgetown University, in Washington, D.C.

DHEP proved to be invaluable for the development of Sentara's Ethics Program. John C. Fletcher, at that time Director of the Center for Biomedical Ethics; Edward M. Spencer, Director of Outreach Programs; and Ann E. Mills, Associate Director of Outreach Programs—all faculty members at the Center for Biomedical Ethics—had developed DHEP from a practical perspective, with the expectation that participants would design clearly defined processes for clinical ethics activities and organization ethics activities within their organizations.

In spring 1997, the Corporate Ethics Committee renamed itself the Sentara Ethics Advisory Council (SEAC). The new name more accurately reflects the "advisory" purpose of the council. The council focused first on the steps needed to bring a meaningful program into reality. Council members held mentoring discussions with Fletcher, Spencer, and Mills during the next few months. During one of these discussions, Spencer outlined for SEAC his ideal concept of a reporting structure for a system-wide ethics program. He identified an important issue: if an organization ethics program is going to be effective, it must report directly to the governing board. After some discussion, SEAC agreed. Up until then, Sentara ethics committees and the SEAC had provided a quiet, passive service of consultation, information, and education for a few interested individuals. This new proposal represented a radically new approach. Because SEAC had not previously reported its activities to top management, few people knew about its activities. And because people did not know about the council, they could not support it. A well-defined reporting structure would help SEAC garner support for the activities associated with the ethics program throughout the Sentara organization. SEAC members realized that Sentara had to take this major step if the ethics program they envisioned was to be effective in the Sentara organization.

DEVELOPING A COMPREHENSIVE ETHICS PROGRAM
    In fall 1998, SEAC met for a one-day planning retreat to develop a vision of a comprehensive ethics program to satisfy short-term and long-term needs and to identify the infrastructure that would be required to support such a program. The council accomplished a significant amount of work during this retreat. SEAC made the critically important decision to develop an effective reporting structure. SEAC would be responsible for a comprehensive ethics program in Sentara. It would report to the Medical Affairs Committee (MAC), which is made up of members of the board of directors, senior administrators, and medical directors from the organizations throughout Sentara. Two vice presidents, Darleen Anderson and Lois Kercher, members of SEAC, took the proposal to the MAC and received approval for the creation of the new reporting structure. Reporting to the board of directors through the MAC was essential to ensure SEAC's credibility.
    During this retreat, SEAC developed its mission statement and purpose statement, which served as the blueprint for the rest of the program. SEAC's mission statement is as follows:
- Support the ethical and professional delivery of high-quality healthcare services to the community.
- Be responsible for Sentara Healthcare's Ethics Program.
- Provide clinical and organization consultation services.
- Provide an educational service for clinical, professional, and organizational ethics.
- Support the institutional review boards and the ethics program's activities in research.

SEAC's four-fold purpose statement is as follows:
- Support the ethical climate across the HCO.
- Work to define options for those making difficult ethical decisions

- Provide a forum for dialogue, clarification, consensus, recommendations, policy review, and education related to the ethics of healthcare.
- Work with patients, families, physicians, healthcare professionals, and the community.

SEAC's mission and purpose statements were developed within the context of Sentara's core values. These values and their intents are:

- *Service:* Serve our community and its people with skill, concern, and dedication.
- *Quality:* Achieve excellence in everything we do with competence and compassion.
- *People:* Treat people with utmost respect, dignity, and courtesy.
- *Stewardship:* Use our resources wisely and hold ourselves accountable for good financial management.
- *Integrity:* Be honest and fair in all our relationships.

SEAC identified three areas of focus for its activities: clinical consultations, professional ethics, and organization ethics. SEAC drafted a budget for anticipated expenses that allowed appropriate personnel to pursue education efforts and supported the operational supplies that the program needed.

SECOND STEPS: DEVELOPING ACTIVITIES FOR CLINICAL ETHICS, PROFESSIONAL ETHICS, AND ORGANIZATION ETHICS

SEAC's first focus is clinical ethics. Clinical ethics committees and associated ethics consultation services have been a feature of Sentara's acute-care facilities for a number of years. Nonhospital divisions within Sentara have benefited from these hospital clinical ethics consultation services. The development of new internal ethics committees was initiated by Sentara Health Management and Sentara Mental Health Management (the organization's health plan division) and by Sentara Senior WellCare (a community-based program for senior citizens).

Policy development and review are an important function of Sentara's ethics committees. For instance, policies regarding the Health Care Financing Administration (HCFA) and JCAHO's Standards for Patient Rights and Organization Ethics are reviewed and revised by the ethics committee of each hospital before they are sent for approval from administration, patient care communities, and the medical staff of each hospital. This process ensures that ethics committees are involved in policy development.

Education is a major concern of each of the ethics committees in Sentara's hospitals. For instance, members of the ethics committees who offer consultation services are required to receive a minimum of six contact hours per year in clinical ethics education. SEAC facilitates this by offering three eight-hour educational sessions every third year. These sessions are structured on the *Introduction to Clinical Ethics,* a textbook edited by John Fletcher and others.[2] During alternate years, SEAC offers one eight-hour educational session to committee members. Ethics committee members engage in a continual process of education by attending program offerings from other HCOs and academic institutions, and through selected readings and discussions. Ethics committee members assess their educational needs through a survey that is used by SEAC to develop, coordinate, and publicize appropriate and consistent educational offerings to staff throughout the Sentara community.

Professional ethics is SEAC's second focus. Sentara's mission is to provide excellent patient care, but conflicts in perspectives may undermine this mission. The challenge is twofold: to promote an understanding of professional codes of ethics by all Sentara staff and to promote an understanding of what these codes may mean in individual and organizational decision making. For instance, financial constraints and conflicts of interest may affect clinical decision making and erode or undermine a professional's integrity. These situations can only lead to cynicism, which may adversely affect patient care. The SEAC offers forums for discussion among professionals that emphasize the importance of understanding the needs of all the stakeholders in the organization and of balancing those needs with the needs of the organization as a whole.

Organization ethics is the SEAC's third area of focus. The U.S. Department of Justice's concern regarding fraud and abuse in healthcare has meant that HCOs must attend to compliance activities, and Sentara's Integrity Program was developed to respond to those concerns. SEAC acts as a resource for the Integrity Program by providing organization ethics consultations for issues not clarified by compliance requirements. The consultation service is available when entities within the organization request assistance with the evaluation of decisions that involve ethics issues. The response to this service has been positive.

TAKING BIGGER STEPS

Until 1998, SEAC was composed of employees who volunteered their time. In 1998 the first full-time employee for ethics, Julia Milner West, was appointed. She is the co-chair of SEAC, provides clinical ethics consultation service to four hospitals, and is responsible for the coordination of the Sentara Healthcare Ethics Program. The ethics program continues to be supported by volunteer employees within the organization.

THE TURNING POINT

In 1999, SEAC held its second annual one-day retreat, where members reviewed the year's work and more clearly defined the activities of the ethics program. They identified research, evaluation, and performance improvement as areas in which progress had not been made. SEAC members believed it would be appropriate to develop instruments that would allow measurement of perceived ethical "gaps" in the culture of the organization and to measure the effectiveness of the tools that were designed to close those gaps.

REPORTING

The SEAC chairman, Earl D. White, II, gave the first report to the MAC in 1999 and the second in 2000. Both reports documented a detailed overview of the current activities of the ethics program. White reports to the MAC on a quarterly basis and submits an annual review.

2000 AND BEYOND: AN EXPANDING VISION

The Sentara Healthcare Ethics Program attracted interest from the Sentara community and other HCOs. In January 2000, Sentara leadership and SEAC decided to establish the Sentara Center for Healthcare Ethics. By designating a "center for healthcare ethics," medical and administrative leadership in Sentara Healthcare sent a message to the organization's internal and external communities that Sentara takes ethics in healthcare seriously.

Communication is a vital part of the work of the center. A quarterly newsletter, *Ethics, Human Values, & Medicine,* has been developed and is distributed to Sentara staff and professionals via electronic mail. Articles of interest include ethics issues in acute care, long-term care, home healthcare, hospice care, managed care, managed mental health; professional ethics; and clinical case discussions. The newsletter provides information about the Virginia Healthcare Decisions Act and advance directive information that can be used by professional healthcare providers in any setting.

A website is planned to provide an effective communication link for the center. Sentara Healthcare maintains a comprehensive internal computer network for a large number of its employees, linking them via electronic mail. This Intranet computer system has its own internal website, *WaveNet,* which houses many sites within the organization. SEAC is in the process of developing its own website through this communication tool. SEAC plans to include on the website information about the activities of the center, including educational forums, information for advance directive planning, and policies and procedures of the Sentara Healthcare Ethics Program. The website will be linked to Sentara's home page and the Integrity Program, for a comprehensive overview of Sentara's organization ethics activities. The website will provide a handbook for the Center and the Ethics Program, which can be printed out. In the future, the center anticipates the development of an external website that will link Sentara's home page and the Integrity Program so that information on the center's activities can be shared within the organization and the community.

PERSONAL OBSERVATIONS

The Sentara Center for Healthcare Ethics is fortunate to have the support of Sentara leadership. This support has allowed the center to devote time and resources to the formulation of its goals and to understand more clearly and define its roles, duties, and responsibilities within the context of providing an ethics infrastructure for Sentara Healthcare.

Anyone in the healthcare world knows how fast things can change. To retain the credibility that the Sentara Healthcare Ethics Program has attained over the past couple of years, it must be able to meet the challenges of change within the context of Sentara's expectations for it and within the context of Sentara's mission and values. For instance, the research world is changing radically. The implications of these changes will almost certainly impact Sentara's institutional review boards (IRBs), which exist to oversee Sentara's research activities. The Ethics Program must be able to support the organization's IRBs so the IRBs can respond to new responsibilities and regulations.

The future will be a time of change and challenge, providing an opportunity for creativity as well as service to Sentara Healthcare and the community. Research ethics, telemedicine, reproductive medicine, economic ethics, and the ethical issues in the provision of day-to-day care of patients will continue to challenge the Ethics Program's thinking and ethics processes.

The more that the Ethics Program provides timely, intelligent, reflective, proactive, and pre-emptive educational and consultation services, the more it will be called to be a presence for the organization. The members of the Ethics Program are gratified to be part of a process through which some of the dilemmas in their healthcare community can be addressed and discussed, enabling them to participate in resolution.

NOTES

1. Information on Sentara Healthcare can be found at <http://www.sentara.com>.

2. J.C. Fletcher et al., ed., *Introduction to Clinical Ethics,* 2nd ed. (Hagerstown, Md.: University Publishing Group, 1997).

Appendix D

Making the Most of Disequilibrium: Bridging the Gap between Clinical and Organizational Ethics in a Newly Merged Healthcare Organization

Catherine Myser, Patricia Donehower, and Cathy Frank

INTRODUCTION

The year 1995 set a record for hospital mergers and acquisitions,[1] including the merger that resulted in the formation of our own healthcare organization, Fletcher Allen Health Care (FAHC), in Burlington, Vermont.[2] In our experience and that of others, a merger creates an opportunity for truly transforming institutional change and expansion.[3] Indeed, institutional evolution can be regarded as a continuum, punctuated alternatively by periods of equilibrium and disequilibrium. Our thesis is that a merger is a period of disequilibrium that can lead to a more comprehensive organizational ethics infrastructure[4] when properly harnessed. Herein we describe how FAHC made the most of such disequilibrium by building a more comprehensive and better integrated ethics infrastructure, bridging the gap between clinical and organizational ethics.[5] At FAHC, our overall goal is to develop an ethics infrastructure that enables the organization at all levels of operation to recognize and manage ethical issues.

In our case, bridging the gap between clinical and organizational ethics has been a three-stage process. The first stage (1995 through 1998) led to the creation of the Board of Trustees Ethics Committee as a complement to the existing Clinical Ethics Committee.[6] The second stage (1998) involved hiring a director of ethics to build and lead a comprehensive ethics program at FAHC and the University of Vermont College of Medicine. During this stage, we also formed the FAHC Ethics Task Force to determine what ethics infrastructure might be necessary to meet the evolving clinical and organizational ethics needs of an integrated healthcare organization. In the third stage (1999 and beyond), the FAHC corporate officers will implement the Ethics Task Force's recommendation to create an Organizational Ethics Council.

This chapter focuses primarily on the second stage and hints at where FAHC intends to go in the third stage. We only briefly summarize the first stage, because the evolution of the Board of Trustees Ethics Committee will be addressed in a future publication.

STAGE 1:
CLARIFYING THE ETHICS MISSION

Our 1995 merger joined four organizations with diverse cultures in a precarious balance: a 500-bed tertiary-care teaching hospital associated with the University of Vermont College of Medicine; ten independent practice groups (including 250 full-time physicians) formerly comprising the University of Vermont College of Medicine University Health Center; an eighty-three-bed Catholic community hospital; and a managed-care organization. To alleviate some merger-induced tensions— including conflicting cultures, fear of practices involving cost controls, lack of trust, and feared loss of a "caring environment"—FAHC began clarifying a unified mission. As part of this process, FAHC merged the traditional clinical ethics committees of the two hospitals. However, the merger task force believed that the newly merged Clinical Ethics Committee might be ill equipped to address increasingly complex issues involving resource allocation, especially at the system or corporate level of decision making. For this and other reasons, the new Board of Trustees Ethics Committee was formed[7] under corporate bylaws to "discuss, review, and recommend on matters relating to professional, economic, and humanitarian value-based issues."[8]

The Board of Trustees Ethics Committee took several important steps to bridge the gap between clinical and organizational ethics following the merger. These steps included (1) engaging senior management and the board to have a voice in ethics and providing a minimal ethics education program at the highest levels of the organization; and (2) initiating a search for the first professional ethicist in the institution. Policies reviewed by the Board of Trustees Ethics Committee in its first year included a conflict-of-interest contract for medical staff, a preferred-business-partner policy for not-for-profit institutions, advice on indigent care, advice on reduction in work force, and a policy on confidentiality in telemedicine.

STAGE 2:
TESTING THE ETHICS INFRASTRUCTURE

Despite these achievements, both the Board of Trustees Ethics Committee and the Clinical Ethics Committee experienced growing confusion and dysfunction by the third year after the merger. Because three different chief executive officers led the organization in its first three years, there was a general lack of continuity. This administrative turnover resulted in periodic disconnection between the Board of Trustees Ethics Committee and senior-level administrators. Ethics took a back seat as leadership concentrated on redesigning the organization, dealing with budget issues, reducing the work force, dealing with a nursing union drive, and maintaining quality of care. Issues with ethical implications were not recognized as such and not referred to the Board of Trustees Ethics Committee. For example, managers felt pressure and value conflicts as a result of extreme changes in staffing and delivery of care, but they did not seek input or assistance from the Board of Trustees Ethics Committee. Also, the committee was unprepared to assist with certain types of ethical issues such as whether high-cost therapies should be offered despite third-party payers' refusal to reimburse.

The Clinical Ethics Committee was adversely affected by frequent turnover in leadership. For example, the president of the medical staff changed every year, and the committee had difficulty recruiting and retaining leaders for the committee from the active physicians. The number of consultation requests was diminishing, and the consulting, policy, and education subcommittees lacked clear goals and adequate organizational resources. In addition, the overlapping roles and functions of the two committees presented difficulties.

After reading the ethics literature, attending ethics conferences, and seeking the advice of other medical institutions, administrators at FAHC concluded that the expertise of a professional ethicist was of critical importance to the organization. They realized that the organization could no longer rely on occasional guest speakers on ethics or brief visits by ethicists. To help address the problems mentioned above, the institution hired a full-time director of ethics in January 1998. However, FAHC had no clear understanding of a professional ethicist's role, training, expertise, or potential contributions (especially in relation to what others in different disciplines could make), and no clear understanding of standards of practice in the field of ethics. Further, the institution did not clearly define the role of the director of ethics in relation to the Board of Trustees Ethics Committee and the Clinical Ethics Committee. Finally, the director's joint appointment to FAHC (80 percent) and to the University of Vermont College of Medicine (20 percent) set the stage for competition among the various constituencies.

Most significantly, controversy arose over who would do clinical ethics consultations. Within a few months of the institution's hiring a professional ethicist, requests for clinical ethics consultations increased dramatically. Physicians and others became comfortable with the expert consultation model and embraced this new service. However, the consultation subcommittee of the Clinical Ethics Committee, which had previously performed consultations, was left without a real role and consequently felt alienated. There was general confusion about the future role of the Clinical Ethics Committee. After several months of tension, the Board of Trustees Ethics Committee, the Clinical Ethics Committee, the director of ethics, and other institutional leaders agreed that it was time to rethink the overall ethics infrastructure at FAHC.

GAPS BETWEEN INSTITUTIONAL ETHICS NEEDS AND INFRASTRUCTURE

The hiring of a professional ethicist at FAHC precipitated a preliminary analysis of ethics needs and a comprehensive analysis of successes and failures of the existing ethics infrastructure. As a first step, the institution identified specific gaps between the espoused goals of each committee and what each was able to achieve. These gaps were classified into four categories: lack of understanding regarding ethics, lack of political support, structural constraints, and unevaluated outcomes.

Lack of Understanding Regarding Ethics

Committee members received no formal ethics education, but some members were self-educated and some had received training on end-of-life decision making, in order to lead case-based ethics education discussions. Most committee members, however, had only a minimal understanding of ethics as a formal discipline and of its potential contributions to the identification and management of problems at the clinical and organizational levels. Accordingly, the institution had no substantive selection criteria for committee members based on relevant knowledge, skills, and expertise. Other than ensuring representation from various disciplines, genuine interest was the sole selection criterion. In addition, various members of the organization had differing and even competing definitions and expectations of "ethics" and "ethical expertise." There was little ethics education for students and no continuing education for healthcare practitioners, administrators, or trustees.

Lack of Political Support

The administration and the broader community at FAHC did not show enough ownership of or investment in ethics resources, and this lack of support was especially apparent for the Clinical Ethics Committee. This was partly a communication and public relations problem of the Clinical Ethics Committee and partly a broader administrative and institutional culture problem. As a result, ethical issues were not effectively managed because the committee was not able to bring these issues to administrators at the right departmental or institutional levels.

Structural Constraints

The Clinical Ethics Committee at FAHC, like other traditional hospital ethics committees, was not well equipped to manage the overlapping clinical and organizational ethics issues that arose during the first three years of the new integrated healthcare system, for example, policy issues related to managed care and limiting access to more expensive treatment. This committee could not easily reflect on structural professional or institutional constraints (sometimes referred to as the "hidden curriculum")[9] on the identification and management of ethical issues. For example, in a traditional medical hierarchy, nurses, medical students, and even residents are not always fully able to function as moral agents, and yet this is not always recognized or addressed as an "ethical" issue. Thus, the committee's effectiveness began to "level off." Although the Board of Trustees Ethics Committee enjoyed some initial success, this first-stage evolution was not sufficient to address evolving clinical and organizational ethics issues, such as business and research ethics issues resulting from partnerships with for-profit organizations. In addition, the board committee could not provide adequate outreach to the institution's satellites and affiliates.

Unevaluated Outcomes

Before the arrival of the director of ethics, FAHC had conducted no systematic ethics needs assessment at the departmental or institutional level. The goals and objectives of the Clinical Ethics Committee and the Board of Trustees Ethics Committee were not specific enough, and the committees had done nothing to measure their outcomes and effectiveness. For example, ethics policies were not always disseminated or put into practice, and educational initiatives and consultations were not evaluated to assess their effectiveness. It was necessary to conduct a system-wide ethics needs assessment, to set clear goals, and to develop appropriate measures to assess the effectiveness of outcomes. It was clearly time for the committees to look at the bigger picture.

ETHICS TASK FORCE

By agreement of the Clinical Ethics Committee, the Board of Trustees Ethics Committee, the director of ethics, and the institutional administration, the FAHC Ethics Task Force[10] was commissioned by the chair of the FAHC Board of Trustees in September 1998. Its charge was to examine the ethics needs of the institution systematically and to propose a new ethics infrastructure to meet the comprehensive demands of an integrated healthcare organization. The needs assessment had two components: (1) a series of meetings of Ethics Task Force members with a range of stakeholders at FAHC and the University of Vermont College of Medicine,[11] and (2) a content analysis of the eighty-five ethics consultations conducted by the director of ethics since her arrival in January 1998.

As a result of these meetings with stakeholders, the Ethics Task Force identified a series of themes, which can be summarized broadly as educational and cultural issues.

1. Educational Issues. Stakeholders acknowledged a general misunderstanding about what "ethics" actually is. In many cases, staff believed they lacked the ability to recognize ethical issues consistently; they also believed they lacked the knowledge base and skills to make solid and defensible ethical decisions, especially in the face of competing obligations. Thus, staff expressed a strong need and desire for formal ethics education, as well as concern about the disparity between the formal and informal curriculum and practice in ethics.

2. Cultural Issues. The Ethics Task Force identified two cultural issues. First, all healthcare professionals who spoke with the task force expressed a desire for a nonthreatening environment in which to discuss and explore difficult ethical questions. Respondents were genuinely concerned that ethics had little visibility and little priority at FAHC. They believed that it was essential to integrate ethics proactively and with an emphasis on prevention into all individual and group decision making at the institution. Second, some nursing and allied health pro-

---

Exhibit 1: Clinical Ethics Issues

- Withholding and withdrawal of treatment
- Defining and applying the concepts of best interest, quality of life, and futility
- Ethical management of uncertain diagnoses and/or prognoses
- Confusion or conflict regarding the scope and application of DNR orders and advance directives (especially across state lines, and especially when multiple versions exist)
- Challenges in the informed-consent process, including assessment of capacity and management of "waxing and waning" capacity
- Substituted decision making
- Distinguishing and balancing ethical and legal decisions
- Discontinuity of care
- Physician-assisted suicide
- Confidentiality
- Discharges against medical advice
- Team and patient/family mistrust and conflict
- Poor communication around values

fessionals, and some medical students, expressed uneasiness about possible negative repercussions if they expressed a concern about ethics or
requested an ethics consultation—especially in cases where their supe-
riors made requests or orders that conflicted with respondents' personal
or professional codes of ethics. Some attending physicians and residents likewise said they did not always feel free to raise questions about
ethics, because they feared that doing so might be interpreted as admitting a lack of knowledge or skill in a professional culture that does not
always welcome questioning or admission of mistakes or errors.[12]

An evaluation of consultations conducted by the director of ethics
during her first eighteen months at FAHC offered an additional source
of data to determine what kinds of ethical issues and needs were being
raised at the institution.[13] These included traditional clinical ethics issues (see exhibit 1) and organizational ethics issues (see exhibit 2).

STAGE 3:
RE-ENGINEERING ETHICS

During the third stage of the process of bridging the gap between
clinical and organizational ethics at FAHC, the institution began to address the specific gaps identified regarding the existing ethics infrastructure, as well as the institutional ethics needs identified by the Ethics Task Force and in the ethics consultation process.

INCREASED ETHICS EDUCATION

It was essential to the work and recommendations of the Ethics Task
Force to set out a clear definition of *ethics* and to overcome a variety of
common misperceptions about ethics and ethics expertise. The Ethics
Task Force clarified that ethics does not mean merely being in compliance; is not telling people what to do; is not doing what feels right; is
not following good instincts; and is not virtuousness, religion, good
manners, psychological counseling, social work, or professionalism.
Rather, it is the branch of philosophy involving ethical theories (for
example, utility-based, duty-based, virtue-based, community-based, or

---

Exhibit 2: Organizational Ethics Issues

- Questions from human resources about managing "abusive" employees and about changing employee ben-
  efits
- Reproductive issues raised by merger with a Roman Catholic institution
- Issues of business and research ethics resulting from partnerships with for-profit organizations
- Institutional policies related to limiting access to more expensive treatments
- Bequeaths to FAHC and possible ethical obligations to affected intimates
- Policy issues related to managed care

---

care-based theories), principles (for example, autonomy, beneficence, nonmaleficence, justice, and solidarity), and concepts (for example, best interests, quality of life, and futility), which, in addition to basic logic and critical reasoning skills, serve as important tools for identifying and managing value conflicts. The Ethics Task Force recommended permanent institutional support for a professional ethicist, formally trained in philosophy and bioethics, to build and lead an ethics program at FAHC[14] and the University of Vermont College of Medicine.

To address the need to provide ethics education for FAHC staff (including those on its ethics committees) and University of Vermont healthcare faculty and students, the task force urged the creation of a comprehensive and consistent ethics education program, well integrated into ongoing organizational activities, to provide a consistent ethical framework for clinical and organizational decision making. This ethics education program would develop an understanding of ethics as a professional discipline, providing a solid foundation of ethics knowledge and skills as core tools for healthcare professionals and administrators alike.

In the first major educational initiative following the task force's recommendations, the director of ethics sent fourteen FAHC and University of Vermont healthcare practitioners and administrators[15] to the intensive bioethics course at Georgetown University's Kennedy Institute of Ethics in June 1999. The goal of this initiative was to equip clinical, educational, and organizational leaders with a basic foundation of ethics knowledge and skills, better preparing them to collaborate with the director of ethics to advance institutional ethics goals and initiatives.[16] The initial efforts of these intensive bioethics course attendees from FAHC and the University of Vermont were to target (1) "hot spots" identified in ethics consultations (for example, education and policy development around clinical ethics issues in the various intensive care units); (2) ethics needs identified in Ethics Task Force stakeholders meetings, beginning with the development of an evolved organizational ethics infrastructure at FAHC; and (3) the development of an interprofessional ethics course involving faculty from the University of Vermont College of Medicine, its schools of allied health and nursing, and its department of social work.

BOLSTERING POLITICAL SUPPORT

The Ethics Task Force used several strategies to address the political problem of a lack of shared ownership and investment in ethics. First, the Ethics Task Force was formed to evaluate FAHC's ethics infrastructure and to identify any unaddressed ethics needs. This was done because the institution recognized the necessity of acknowledging both the strengths and weaknesses of its current ethics committees, especially as they were being challenged by the increasingly complex and overlapping clinical and organizational ethics issues described above. Second, the composition of the Ethics Task Force was designed to include key FAHC administrators and a balanced group of stakeholders. One goal in doing so was to engage the individuals (and the interested groups they represented) in identifying concerns and in developing creative, positive, and ongoing solutions. Third, the Ethics Task Force solicited input from all of the major stakeholders, through a needs-assessment process (fall/winter 1998) and the "buy-in" process (spring/summer 1999) that included regular meetings, circulation of multiple drafts of its report and recommendations, and articles and updates in the FAHC newsletter. The formation, composition, and process of the Ethics Task Force generated interest in bridging the gap between clinical and organizational ethics. The Ethics Task Force also opened up communication regarding ethics generally at FAHC, to create an open and non-threatening atmosphere that encouraged and supported the recognition and management of ethics issues at all levels. This process made it clear that it was necessary to strengthen the FAHC's ethics infrastructure.

IMPROVED STRUCTURE

Neither the Clinical Ethics Committee nor the Board of Trustees Ethics Committee (nor the two working in tandem) had been equipped to manage the evolving and overlapping clinical and organizational ethics issues associated with an integrated healthcare system. Thus, the Ethics Task Force proposed the creation of the FAHC Organizational Ethics Council specifically tailored to meet this need (see exhibit 3). This new committee was a natural evolution of the institution's ethics infrastructure, which now also included a professional clinical and organizational ethics consultation service assigned to the director of ethics.

In addition, the Ethics Task Force urged the organization to main-

---

Exhibit 3: Responsibilities of the FAHC Organizational Ethics Council

---

20. Facilitate ethics policy development by:
   1. identifying clinical and organizational policy needs at the point of service,
   2. organizing the appropriate people to develop solutions, and
   3. shepherding the policy through the approval process.
21. Support the Director of Ethics in the development of programs to meet ethics education needs at the point of service.
22. Sponsor periodic multidisciplinary discussion forums to explore ethical issues of general concern at FAHC.

Note: In all these activities, the Organizational Ethics Council's emphasis would be to facilitate local solutions to local problems, to engage more stakeholders in ethics policy development and education affecting them, and to engage in broader overall outreach.

tain the Board of Trustees Ethics Committee as defined by FAHC by-laws, with a renewed commitment to ensuring ethics attention and involvement at the board level. For example, organizational ethics consultations might first be brought to the director of ethics; if additional expertise were required, the case would be referred to the Organizational Ethics Council and the Board of Trustees Ethics Committee for broader discussion. The Board of Trustees Ethics Committee would work with the FAHC Board of Trustees to ensure that a comprehensive ethics program remains a visible priority in FAHC's strategic plan, and that adequate financial and human resources are allocated to facilitate its activities.

The Ethics Task Force noted that, as a result of the changes in the FAHC ethics infrastructure, it had become necessary to redefine the Clinical Ethics Committee. The decision as to whether this committee would still be needed (and, if so, how its structure and functions would be redefined to integrate into this new organizational ethics infrastructure) was left to the Medical Staff Executive Committee (with advice from the Clinical Ethics Committee).

The Ethics Task Force recommended that members of the Organizational Ethics Council, who would be selected according to their positional knowledge and skills,[17] should receive basic training in clinical and organizational ethics theories, principles, and concepts. Thus, the Ethics Task Force specifically proposed an Organizational Ethics Council with a larger focus and membership than a traditional hospital ethics committee, better equipping it to reflect on professional, institutional, and structural constraints to the identification and management of ethics issues and to address overlapping clinical and organizational ethics issues. In addition, with the inclusion of more senior clinical and organizational leaders in its membership, the Organizational Ethics Council would manage ethical issues at the appropriate departmental and institutional levels.

EVALUATING ETHICS AS QUALITY IMPROVEMENT

To address the lack of attention to measures and outcomes of ethics education, policy development, and consultation, the Ethics Task Force advised the integration and systematic evaluation of such activities at the clinical and organizational level as part of the quality improvement program at FAHC. The task force recommended that the determination and evaluation of measures for ethics activities should be the mutual responsibility of the Ethics Program and the Quality Council.[18] To ensure this practical link between ethics and quality improvement activities, the task force favored a reporting structure linking the Organizational Ethics Council, the Quality Council, and the Board of Trustees Ethics Committee. In addition, the task force endorsed the idea that the director of ethics serve as a member of the Quality Council. These suggestions of the Ethics Task Force represent yet more strategies for making ethics visible at the proper institutional levels for effective management. The task force hopes that feedback over time will fuel continuous improvement of patient care and organizational decision making throughout this integrated healthcare institution.

CONCLUSION

We cannot predict what the future will bring for FAHC or for similar systems being formed via mergers across the nation. We are optimistic that we have made advances in bridging the gap between clinical and organizational ethics. Thus, FAHC serves as one example that organizational upheaval and crisis following a merger can create an exciting opportunity for transformative institutional change and growth that benefits the healthcare organization, patients, and the community.

NOTES

This chapter is reprinted from *The Journal of Clinical Ethics* 10, no. 3; © 1997, *The Journal of Clinical Ethics;* used with permission.

1. S. Lutz, "1995: A Record Year for Hospital Deals," *Modern Healthcare* 25, no. 51 (1995): 43.

2. Fletcher Allen Health Care is named after two women, Mary Fletcher and Fanny Allen.

3. P.B. Hofmann, "Hospital Mergers and Acquisitions: A New Catalyst for Examining Organizational Ethics," *Bioethics Forum* 12, no. 2 (1998): 46.

4. D.O. Renz and W.B. Eddy, "Organizations, Ethics, and Health Care: Building an Ethics Infrastructure for a New Era," *Bioethics Forum* 12, no. 2 (1998): 29-39.

5. "The growing edge is the new frontier of organizational ethics. Although it has been there all the while, only recently has it become the cauldron of ferment and change." R.L. Potter, "From Clinical Ethics to Organizational Ethics: The Second Stage of the Evolution of Bioethics," *Bioethics Forum* 12, no. 2 (1998): 3.

6. The Clinical Ethics Committee is locally referred to as the Medical Staff Ethics Advisory Committee.

7. The chair of the Board of Trustees Ethics Committee served on the Clinical Ethics Committee, and four members of the Clinical Ethics Committee served on the Board of Trustees Ethics Committee.

8. Board of Trustees Ethics Committee members include four FAHC Board of Trustee members; the president of the medical staff; four members from the Clinical Ethics Committee (including its chair); one individual knowledgeable in Judeo-Christian values; and others who have knowledge of other cultures, beliefs, and values. The chair of the FAHC Board of Trustees, chief executive officer of FAHC, and president of the medical staff are *ex officio* members.

9. F.W. Hafferty and R. Franks, "The Hidden Curriculum, Ethics Teaching, and the Structure of Medical Education," *Academic Medicine* 69, no. 11 (1994): 861-71.

10. The chief medical officer appointed the members of the Ethics Task Force, which included two FAHC Board of Trustee members, the chief financial officer, the chief medical officer, the chief nursing officer, the director of ethics, the college of medicine's dean of education, a nurse educator, two former chairs of the premerger Clinical Ethics Committees (one physician and one nurse), the director of spiritual services, and the corporate liaison sponsor of the Catholic Health Care System. Three of these task force members were also members of the Clinical Ethics Committee, and four were also members of the Board of Trustees Ethics Committee (including its chair).

11. These stakeholders include the FAHC Board of Trustees, the Board of Trustees Ethics Committee, the Medical Staff Executive Committee, the Clinical Ethics Committee, the Nursing Shared Governance Council, two University of Vermont IRBs, and the University of Vermont College of Medicine Instructional Design Committee.

12. C. Bosk, *Forgive and Remember: Managing Medical Failure* (Chicago, Ill.: University of Chicago Press, 1979).

13. Approximately 40 percent of all consultations were requested by attending physicians. Residents and nurses each requested an additional 22 percent of all consultations. Patients and families, administrators, and other healthcare professionals and staff requested the remaining 16 percent. Approximately 30 percent of all consultations involved patients in various intensive care units.

14. In 1997, the Board of Trustees approved a policy supporting the creation and ongoing financial support of the Ethics Program at FAHC.

15. FAHC sent a risk manager, two nurse administrators (one from the Visiting Nurse Association), a social worker, the director of patient relations, and the director of quality monitoring and improvement. The University of Vermont sent the dean of medical education, the dean of primary care, an associate professor of surgery, an assistant professor of internal medicine, the director of inpatient psychiatry, an assistant professor of nursing, the dean of allied health, and an associate professor of allied health.

16. One participant reflected, "We have moved from unconscious incompetence in ethics to conscious incompetence in ethics, and that is an important advance toward learning."

17. Membership of the Organizational Ethics Council suggested by the Ethics Task Force included two physicians (one from FAHC and one from the community); two nurses (one hospital-based, one outpatient); the director of ethics; one representative each from risk management, patient relations, pastoral care, pharmacy, human resources, quality improvement, social work, and senior management; an education expert; and two at-large members with relevant expertise (e.g., experts in business ethics or organizational development). The Ethics Task Force advised that the Organizational Ethics Council chair be appointed by the chief medical officer from among the committee's members.

18. The members of the Quality Council are the chief executive officer, the chief medical officer, the chief nursing officer, the chief financial officer, the senior vice president/medical director, the director of quality/monitoring/improvement, the vice president of quality and care management, and the director of human resources.

Appendix E

Fulfilling Institutional Responsibilities in Healthcare: Organizational Ethics and the Role of Mission Discernment

John A. Gallagher and Jerry Goodstein

INTRODUCTION

Change has been an endemic feature of American healthcare throughout the twentieth century. Hospitals have grown from community institutions caring for the homeless and dying into modern technological corporations. Where hospitals could once offer only meager forms of palliative care, the contemporary hospital offers the residents of a community an armamentarium of diagnostic and therapeutic interventions undreamed of a century ago. In order to sustain this transition, U.S. hospitals have acquired a corporate structure that is similar to that of commercial enterprises.

The role of the physician has undergone a similar transformation. In the living memory of many Americans, physicians were either general-practice physicians or surgeons. Today the scope of medical practice ranges from family practice and general internal medicine to a vast array of specialties and subspecialties. As new therapies are developed to treat specific diseases and more is learned about specific organ systems, as new technologies make possible the viewing and treatment of discrete aspects of the human body, new specializations arise. These new technologies have altered the role of the physician within the healthcare delivery system. Increasingly, physicians are becoming investors or owners of ambulatory surgery centers, radiology clinics, or heart and birthing hospitals. Many physicians financially benefit not only from the services they provide, but also from the profits of the facility in which they render services.

In addition, the financing of healthcare has also undergone a major transformation. For the first half of the twentieth century, healthcare was financed on a fee-for-service basis. After World War II, Blue Cross-Blue Shield began to offer employers indemnity insurance policies, which could be passed on as benefits to employees. Insurance companies became major payers for healthcare. In the 1960s, Medicare, Medicaid, and other federally subsidized healthcare programs were initiated, and the federal government eventually became the largest single payer of health services in the United States. The 1980s and 1990s were characterized by rapidly escalating healthcare costs and an emphasis upon horizontal and vertical integration among healthcare providers and payers in an effort to contain these costs.

The scope and breadth of this transformation has created a daunting and perplexing array of ethical issues in healthcare and within society at large.[1] The appropriate relationship of physician to patient and the relationship of patient to physician have become unclear[2] and the American public's trust in healthcare providers and the healthcare delivery system has eroded. Healthcare delivery systems are struggling to assess and manage their duties to an ever-expanding array of stakeholders including healthcare professionals, subscribers, and the community.[3]

In the face of these ethical issues, organizational ethics has emerged as a significant concern for healthcare institutions.[4] This essay explores in greater detail the forces that have created organizational ethics issues within healthcare institutions. It emphasizes the importance of mission discernment as a core organizational process that allows healthcare institutions to reflect actively on how to meet the ethical challenges posed by the contemporary healthcare system and to fulfill institutional responsibilities.

THE INTEGRATION
OF AMERICAN HEALTHCARE

The most pervasive trend within the U.S. healthcare delivery system at the turn of the twenty-first century is the concerted effort to achieve horizontal and vertical integration, making the transition from freestanding healthcare organizations to integrated systems. Until recently, the healthcare delivery system was characterized as fragmented—as a series of independent, at times competing, entities that offered divergent and redundant forms of health services to the public. According to Gray, "Until recent years the U.S. health care system could be fairly described in terms of independent nonprofit and small proprietary institutions and of independent physicians practicing alone or in very small groups."[5]

Because the healthcare system was fragmented, it was costly. The proliferation of points of service and the competition between providers were perceived to be the major reasons for the escalation of healthcare expenditures. Patients visited the emergency room for minor complaints that could have been more efficiently addressed in a primary care physician's office, and sought the services of specialists for problems outside their areas of expertise. Hospitals hired staff to support more beds than communities needed and provided services that could be safely and more efficiently offered in outpatient settings. Fee-for-service reimbursement provided an incentive to physicians as well as to hospitals to provide medically unnecessary services and tests. Despite the enormous economic resources allocated to the delivery of health services, a large portion of the American population remained uninsured or underinsured. Morreim reports that in 1929 the cost of healthcare represented 3.9 percent of the Gross National Product. By 1959 that figure had risen only to 4.4 percent. Since that time, the figure has escalated to 14 percent, which translates, in actual dollars, to nearly $2 trillion.[6]

In response to the escalating cost of healthcare and in an effort to enhance the quality and accessibility of healthcare delivery, many healthcare providers (hospitals, physicians, home health services, outpatient sites, diagnostic centers, and long-term care facilities) have attempted to combine in various forms through mergers, joint ventures, and other strategies to achieve horizontal integration.[7] A key goal of horizontal integration is to coordinate the delivery of healthcare to a patient population across a broad continuum of services. Shortell and colleagues suggest that "organized delivery systems (ODS) that have higher levels of functional, physician-system and clinical integration will better meet patient, payer, and community needs."[8] To achieve such integration, it may be necessary to centralize the administration of the various units and to fully integrate physician services within the system.

Vertical integration pertains to the financing of healthcare services. The goal of vertical integration is to control healthcare dollars from the time they enter a system until they are spent on health services. Employers, the federal government, and insurers have a vested interest in controlling healthcare inflation. A variety of programs have been implemented to cap costs and coordinate the delivery of healthcare services. The health-maintenance organization (HMO) is perhaps the clearest example of a vertically integrated healthcare organization. In its pure form, one organization receives premiums to provide health services to a defined population for a contracted period of time. The HMO then allocates a fixed number of dollars across the delivery system to meet the health needs of the defined population for the length of the contract. In other instances, insurance companies market an HMO product and enroll beneficiaries, but then contract with a group of hospitals and physicians or an organized delivery system to provide services.

Commercial insurers have developed a series of initiatives in an effort to control their costs. Instead of paying hospitals on a fee-for-service basis, commercial insurers are now contracting with hospitals for their services. These contracts stipulate the amount of reimbursement hospitals may receive for specific services. In addition, commercial insurers have implemented utilization reviews, which require patients to receive prior approval for hospital and outpatient procedures. Commercial insurers have also entered into contracts with independent physician associations (IPAs) and preferred provider organizations (PPOs). The beneficiaries of the policies must seek the services of a physician within a particular IPA or PPO; otherwise, the beneficiary is responsible for a copayment or the physician's entire bill. Commercial carriers have also begun to provide incentives to physicians within IPAs or PPOs to reduce the number of hospitalizations among their patients and to reduce the number of costly prescriptions and tests. All these techniques fall under the aegis of "managed care."

ETHICAL ISSUES ASSOCIATED WITH INTEGRATION IN HEALTHCARE

The development of horizontally and vertically integrated healthcare delivery systems has led to a plethora of ethical issues. Vertical and horizontal integration potentially increase the concentration of market share among systems and the market power of healthcare systems.[9] At issue is whether corporate power is used to benefit stakeholders or to gain control over healthcare markets.

Physicians and hospitals are increasingly being required to provide patient care within new economic, social, and institutional structures. The responsibility and accountability of physicians has become unfocused. The traditional doctor-patient relationship must now be understood in terms of economic and institutional responsibilities and accountabilities that are opaque at best. Hospitals and physician practices are no longer the centerpieces of the healthcare delivery system, but have become components within an integrated institution.

Integration has resulted in a fundamental shift in focus of the entire healthcare delivery system. Today it is the social and economic institution of the organized delivery system—not physicians and hospitals—that is expected to meet the needs of patients, payers, and communities. The services of physicians and other caregivers are now contextualized and institutionalized within a corporate entity.

Such a development prefigures a number of important changes in healthcare ethics. There has been a major shift away from autonomy as the basic principle of medical ethics and a shift away from the professional autonomy of individual physicians. Reiser sums up this trend as follows: "Individual decision makers are being supplanted by the rules, standards, traditions and collective decision process of organizations, which instruct and construct institutional actions in shaping healthcare choices."[10] In addition, the needs of stakeholders other than patients—specifically payers and the community—assume greater significance. This is a major refocusing of the basic orientation of American healthcare. In the past, the needs of the individual patient were always accepted as the fundamental focus of physician and hospital practice.

For healthcare organizations, a significant ethical challenge is to determine how to fulfill institutional responsibilities to patients, physicians, and other healthcare professionals, payers, and the community. The ethical responsibility and integrity of institutions has already begun to capture the interest of writers in the domains of business ethics and healthcare ethics. Paine argues in favor of broadly focusing attention on the moral issues confronting corporations as opposed to the duties of individuals within corporations.[11] Emanuel, directing his attention to healthcare organizations in particular, has commented: "The physician-patient interaction no longer occurs in a practitioner's office in which the practitioner, alone or in a small group of colleagues, has control over the structures that influence the interaction. Instead these interactions occur within large organizations in which the practitioner or a small group of colleagues does not control 'the rules of engagement.' "[12]

The common theme each of these authors highlights is one echoed in broad terms by Bellah and colleagues, who argue that contemporary American institutions and corporations bear ethical responsibilities.[13] Organizational ethics and mission discernment represent moral activities within integrated healthcare systems to address the ethical issues confronting healthcare institutions. It is the goal of organizational ethics to facilitate institutional and corporate reflection so that an organization can accurately define its ethical responsibilities to stakeholders and then establish processes, policies, and procedures that will enable it to fulfill those responsibilities.

Perhaps the most daunting ethical issues associated with horizontal and vertical integration pertain to the character of the organization that has been created by these processes. Uniting a number of healthcare organizations as well as an array of physicians into an organized delivery system that can deliver quality health services requires reflection on a number of issues. First, there is the question of how power within the integrated system will be used. Second, the quality of partners must be assessed to ensure quality across the system. Third, integration of several hospitals, long-term care organizations, and outpatient facilities into a single organization requires attention to the culture of each of the components. Components of the organization must perform cultural assessments and develop plans to identify and create the desired common culture. Fourth, mergers and acquisitions almost always entail reduction of the workforce somewhere in the new organization. How are the needs of former staff members to be addressed?

ORGANIZATIONAL ETHICS

Organizational ethics is fundamentally concerned with questions of integrity, responsibility, and choice.[14] It involves a comprehensive framework that involves the creation and implementation of processes, procedures, and policies to ensure that the performance of an organization or institution is consistent with its fundamental purpose(s) or ethical aims and values.[15] It is concerned with fulfilling key responsibilities to various stakeholders and ensuring that the choices made on behalf of the institution are responsive to market, financial, and legal realities.

The preservation of institutional integrity is a central focus for organizational ethics. At issue is how to ensure that organizational decisions and actions are carefully considered and implemented in a manner that is consistent with the organization's mission statement and core values. The mission and core values should be an important driving force for an organization,[16] unifying it by providing a common frame of reference and shaping the manner in which opportunities are determined, organizational systems are designed, and decision-making processes are implemented.[17] Such a commitment to core values and institutional integrity is the foundation for long-term organizational success.[18] As Selznick suggests, institutional values are precarious and must be protected: "Institutions embody values, but they can do so only as operative systems or going concerns. The trouble is that what is good for the operative system does not necessarily serve the standards or ideals the institution is supposed to uphold. Therefore institutional values are always at risk. Insofar as organizational, technological, and short-run imperatives dominate decision-making, goals and standards are vulnerable. They are subject to displacement, attenuation, and corruption."[19] Phillips and Margolis underscore this broad point in their efforts to elaborate an ethics for organizations. In particular, they note the manner in which practical demands for effective managerial action and "imperfect originating conditions" (such as the absence of complete freedom and the existence of inequalities in power and status) may lead to the misuse of power in efforts to achieve institutional purpose.[20]

The challenge of sustaining organizational integrity is complicated by the context within which healthcare organizations operate. Healthcare organizations must take into account a variety of internal stakeholders (such as medical staff and employees) and other stakeholders (such as patients, communities, insurers, and government agencies). The current healthcare delivery system is composed of a variety of stakeholders, each with its own self-interests. Physicians, employees, patients, vendors, the civic community, and payers each have their expectations of what the system will do for them. In this environment, stakeholders' conflicting values can make it difficult for an organization to preserve its institutional integrity.[21]

To sustain its organizational integrity, it is crucial for the healthcare organization to acknowledge its multiple stakeholder relationships; the responsibilities it owes to these stakeholders; and the influence of stakeholders on the organization's values, decisions, and actions.[22] Within the past few years, there has been an important call within the literature of healthcare ethics to develop a stronger organizational focus.[23]

This emerging emphasis on organizational ethics in healthcare represents an important departure from much of the healthcare ethics literature. Typically, ethical issues have been addressed from a bioethical perspective that emphasizes issues at the level of the individual, such as decision-making capacity, truth-telling, and confidentiality.[24] Wildes argues that this shift in perspective is essential, given the current environment facing healthcare organizations: "An important area of development for ethics and bioethics, especially in the context of managed care, is to conceive of ethical issues as issues not only for individual persons, but also for systems and social structures as well . . . to situate ethical questions in the web of institutional patterns and relationships."[25]

This "web of institutional patterns and relationships" has been a central focus for business ethics writers, who have directed much of their attention to broad systemic issues such as those associated with corporate behavior in the international business context,[26] the ethics of corporate downsizing,[27] and corporate stakeholder theory.[28]

Organizational ethics departs from the focus on the individual patient who is emphasized in bioethics and from the broad systemic orientation that is emphasized in business ethics, and looks to how the healthcare institution can respond to its responsibilities to multiple stakeholders in a manner that upholds critical institutional purposes and values.[29] It is fundamentally grounded in a "response ethic."[30] That is, healthcare organizations are conceived of as moral agents[31] that respond, answer, and are in dialogue[32] with the multiple organizations; persons; and political, social, and economic forces acting upon them. A response ethic draws on a particular conception of moral agency, one that involves intentionality of purpose and embodiment of values. According to Selznick: "When we view an organization 'as an institution,' we may be mainly concerned with the values it embodies, from the standpoint of the people whose lives it touches as well as that of the larger community. Insofar as it is 'infused with value,' the organization is likely to claim and be granted respect and concern. At the same time, to be an effective participant in the moral order, it must be competent, intentional, and accountable."[33]

Although such a view of moral agency among formal organizations has been disputed,[34] others have emphasized that corporations do have organizational processes and decision-making structures that require a collective sense of responsibility, accountability, and moral agency.[35] Collier points out that while individual agents may make decisions and carry out actions, these individuals do so "in the name of and by the authority of the organization, frequently in contexts where it is not possible to identify and attribute responsibility to any single individual or group."[36]

Operating from a response ethic, an organization is not focused primarily on an abstract notion of the good or the right. A response ethic prompts an organization to find the fitting action or response that embodies its mission, values, and corporate identity in a manner that takes into account the forces acting upon it.[37] Organizational ethics is therefore concerned primarily with concrete notions of the good or the right as these are defined in a particular context.[38]

Organizational ethics is centrally concerned with organizational decision-making processes and choices. Selznick notes that a strategy of responsiveness and fulfillment of core responsibilities in a specific context entails a "burden of choice."[39] There are likely to be tensions and conflicts associated with responsibilities and commitments to multiple stakeholders.[40] It is through the specific choices that a healthcare organization makes (such as its affiliations with other healthcare providers or its budget priorities) and how the institution makes these choices that the character of the institution is defined and institutional integrity is either reinforced or undermined.[41]

One of the goals of organizational ethics is to identify the structures, processes, and policies that support choices that are made in a reflective and responsive manner. Responsiveness is morally bound through consideration of organizational and community values[42] that are grounded in the organization's implicit contract with society.[43] The goal is to foster a certain kind of value-attuned responsiveness[44] or reflexive responsibility.[45] As leadership considers new problems and attempts to meet new stakeholder demands and expectations, choices are made in a manner that sustains commitment to institutional purposes, fulfills key normative responsibilities to stakeholders,[46] and upholds the broader social good.[47]

How can this capacity for institutional responsiveness and responsibility be achieved and built into the social structure of healthcare organizations? Below we discuss one process—mission discernment—created by Holy Cross Health System in South Bend, Indiana.

MISSION DISCERNMENT

DEVELOPING THE MISSION DISCERNMENT PROCESS AT HOLY CROSS HEALTH SYSTEM

The Holy Cross Health System is the parent corporation of seven hospitals/organized delivery systems and one long-term care company. The subsidiary organizations are spread across the United States. In the past, the company had relied upon a document entitled "An Ethical Framework for Corporate Decision Making" to assess major decisions. This document began with a query for decision makers: "How do the alternatives under consideration carry out the mission, core values, and strategic plan of the corporation?" It then focused decision makers' attention on the social vision, multiple responsibilities, and self-interest of the corporation. "An Ethical Framework" was not regarded as "user friendly." Executives expressed confusion about when the document was to be used. Further, they were uncertain about how the decision-assessment process was to be conducted, who was to be involved, and how outcomes were to be reported and to whom. To address these concerns the company developed the mission discernment process.

The president/chief executive officer of the Holy Cross Health system was committed to the goals of integrating the organization's mission more fully into the activities of the organization and to supporting initiatives that would enable the corporate mission statement to be a major influence in decisions shaping the future of the company.[48] The corporation's leaders perceived the mission statement to be the fundamental purpose for the corporation's existence. Decisions inconsistent with its mission could only harm the character of the corporation. The mission discernment process was developed to ensure that the mission of the corporation's member organizations is as much a driver of corporate decisions as financial, marketing, and operational considerations. At the same time that the mission discernment process was being developed, the leadership of the Holy Cross Health System initiated the Organizational Integrity Program (OIP) to ensure that the organization and its staff members were situated within a culture that would enable them to fulfill their legal, ethical, and professional responsibilities. The OIP combines organizational ethics and compliance into an integrated program that focuses on day-to-day operational responsibilities. Whereas the OIP that focuses on operational issues, the mission discernment process is responsible for maintaining the integrity of the organization in its strategic decisions.

Corporate leaders identified the activities of the Corporate Development Division as a key area in which the parent corporation and its subsidiaries interacted on a regular and intense level. Staff in this division reviewed the strategic plans of member organizations annually before submitting these plans to the board of directors. Further, corporate development staff reviewed all capital requests and business plans submitted by member organizations before seeking board approval. Corporate leaders developed the mission discernment process to be an integral part of these ongoing interactions between the corporate office and the member organizations. Thus, although this process would be something new—something additional that the member organizations would have to "deal with"—it was planned to be intricately associated with ongoing activities within the company. The senior vice president for corporate development was a key player in designing and implementing the mission discernment process.

Holy Cross Health System's mission statement reads: "*Faithful* to the spirit of the Congregation of the Sisters of the Holy Cross, the Holy Cross Health System exists to witness to Christ's love through *excellence* in the delivery of health services motivated by respect for those we serve. We foster a climate that *empowers* those who serve with us while *stewarding* our human and financial resources."

Corporate leaders identified the words in italics as key operational words within the mission statement. These words are used to frame major documents and initiatives within the company. They provide the framework for the corporation's vision statement, the themes for annual meetings, the incentive compensation program for subsidiary leadership teams, and the yearly evaluation of corporate staff. The same key words provide the outline of the mission discernment process.

The mission discernment process is used for specific proposals or initiatives under consideration. Initiatives that should go through this process include any major initiative that would affect the self-identity of the organization; any merger, acquisition, or partnership; the addition or deletion of a service line; any initiative that might have a significant impact on the local community; and care of poor or vulnerable populations. Individuals with the relevant capabilities to address the key issues associated with a particular proposal are brought together to deliberate the ethical implications of the proposal. In the first phase of the process, participants assess the consistency between the organization's self-identity and the consequences of a pending decision. Participants are reminded that the purpose of mission discernment is to facilitate corporate decision making in the identification of opportunities for development that are consistent with the mission and self-identity of Holy Cross Health System member organizations. They focus on the key words *fidelity, excellence, empowerment,* and *stewardship.* Under *fidelity,* participants are asked to analyze issues pertaining to the self-identity of the organization as well as potential ethical concerns. Under *excellence,* participants review such issues as the quality of potential partners, or how the quality of health services provided by the organization might be enhanced or undermined by a potential decision. Under *stewardship,* participants incorporate issues associated with strategic planning and financial and legal analysis into the decision-making process.

In the second phase of the mission discernment process, participants inquire about the manner in which a particular proposal is responsive to the interests of the multiple stakeholders who might be affected. The key words in this phase are *empowerment* and *stewardship* of human resources. In this context, participants are charged to assess the impact of a potential decision on patients, employees, other health-care providers, payers, vendors, and other stakeholders. During this phase of the process, participants look outside of the organization at the implications of a pending decision for various persons and groups related to the organization.

The third phase of the mission discernment process directs attention to the health needs of the community. Does a pending decision have a potentially positive or negative impact on the organization's commitment to the care of the poor (uncompensated care), vulnerable populations, community health, or community benefit programs? The key words here, *social justice* and *human dignity,* are drawn, not from the organization's mission statement, but from the core values of the Holy Cross Health System. During this phase in the process, participants consciously address the orgnaization's duties as a not-for-profit, religiously sponsored organization.

The outcome of the mission discernment process is incorporated, with the financial, marketing, and legal analyses associated with the proposal, into a unified business plan. The board of trustees carefully reviews all business plans. The seriousness of the board's commitment to mission discernment is suggested by its announcement that it would table any plan or request for capital allocation that was not accompanied with the outcome of a mission discernment deliberation.

Phillips and Margolis identified *purpose* and *power* as the defining characteristics of corporate moral agency.[49] Mission discernment brings both these characteristics into consideration. The initial purpose of the mission discernment process is to ensure that strategic decisions are consistent with the fundamental purpose—the core business—of the company. A danger faced by Holy Cross Health System, like any other large corporate entity, is its potential to fail to recognize and control its power and self-interest. Strategic plans that are developed by health-care organizations seek to enhance market share, to become strong enough in the market that insurers must contract with them, and to enrich the range and quality of services they provide within a community. Such plans necessarily entail the corporation's self-interest and power. It is for these reasons that the second phase of the mission discernment process requires participants to reflect on the impact of a potential decision on various stakeholders. Of course, the most significant stakeholder is the community from which patients come, but this includes the poor and vulnerable populations within it. The interests of these multiple stakeholders provide a moral barrier to the unrestrained exercise of corporate power. The legitimate interests of stakeholders must be respected and protected. The legitimacy of competing interests must be discerned.

MISSION DISCERNMENT IN PRACTICE

The mission discernment process has been used in a variety of situations within the Holy Cross Health System. The process has assisted the system as it has reviewed and analyzed potential partnerships. In one instance, in which a member organization intended to enter a for-profit enterprise with a group of physicians, the mission discernment process identified the need for this new venture to assume responsibility for community service and care of the poor in its day-to-day operations. In order to accomplish this goal, it was necessary to perform a cultural assessment of both organizations, and both organizations had to agree on the outlines of the culture and priorities of the new organization. Thus, the member organization was able to extend its mission into the life of the organization it was co-creating.

Another discernment addressed what seemed, at the outset, to be an easy issue. A member organization desperately needed to replace its laundry facility. Both the building and the equipment were outdated. The organization identified an opportunity to create a joint venture laundry with several other hospitals, which would have been cost-effective for all parties. The mission discernment process identified an important unrecognized problem—the joint venture would displace the employees of the existing laundry. These employees were minimum-wage staff, and many of them did not have skills to readily find new employment. To protect the welfare of these employees, the organization found a location for the new laundry facility along a major bus line that enabled the employees to work for the new laundry. In this instance, human resource issues and duties to current employees proved to be a major consideration.

A number of mission discernments have been devoted to deliberating the potential effects on the community of developing new sites for service or relocating existing sites. Frequently, the initiative for such

developments is prompted by marketing opportunities. An area is identified as suitable for a new physician practice, an urgent-care center, or
an ambulatory surgery center. The mission discernment process has required the organization to conduct a community needs assessment to
identify the needs of poor and vulnerable populations in a service area.
Thus, the rationale for such an initiative includes not only the creation
of geographic indispensability—an essential characteristic of a successful delivery systems—but also service to the poor, the elderly, patients
with sickle-cell anemia, and other vulnerable groups within a community.

New ventures are not the only focus for mission discernment at
Holy Cross Health System. One of the most complex mission discernments involved a proposal to close an older hospital and to rebuild at a
new site. No other discernment required attention to so many diverse
stakeholders. What would be the impact on the community surrounding the existing facility and the wider civic community? Would the new
location be readily accessible to the elderly patients, Medicaid beneficiaries, and underinsured patients who were dependent upon the existing facility? Various studies were undertaken that demonstrated that
the new site would be as accessible as the existing site. Similar studies
examined the impact of the move on physicians, nurses, and other employees. An impact study was conducted to determine whether the move
would overburden the emergency department of another local hospital;
investigators found that ambulance response times would be reduced
because the two community hospitals would be more geographically
dispersed. In this example, the impact of a corporate decision on stakeholders, ranging from the local and civic communities to other providers, physicians, and staff, was addressed in the mission discernment
process.

The outcomes of these mission discernments indicate the manner
in which corporate decisions can be responsive to marketing, legal, and
financial realities while at the same time addressing the needs of legitimate stakeholders. The process of institutional reflection, embodied
within mission discernment, ensures that mission, finance, marketing,
legal, and other relevant considerations have an appropriate and carefully weighted role in corporate decision making.

Through the mission discernment process, staff members of Holy
Cross Health System are able to identify and respond to the major implications of their proposed initiatives, proactively address ethical issues that might have been ignored or not noted, and fulfill key institutional responsibilities. The ongoing success of the mission discernment
process at Holy Cross Health System represents an explicit institutional
strategy to weave organizational ethics and mission into the fabric of

the organization. The success of these efforts has been sustained by a deep commitment on the part of senior leadership within the organization and the broad participation of administrative and clinical staff.

ETHICAL THEORY AND MISSION DISCERNMENT

An emphasis upon the values of integrity, responsibility, and choice—drawn from ethical theory and closely connected to the core themes of organizational ethics—underlies the development and institutionalization of the mission discernment process. Identifying and indicating the manner in which these values influence the articulation of the process are essential to understanding its moral grounding. The linkage between these values demonstrates that a coherent and justifiable ethical theory is at the center of the mission discernment process.

Integrity should be the basic virtue of healthcare institutions. All healthcare institutions should develop a clearly articulated sense of purpose and ask: What is this organization most fundamentally about? Such a sense of purpose is customarily expressed in an organization's mission statement. The mission statement is the hub that enables an organization to become "a system of consciously coordinated activities."[50] The statement of purpose, or mission statement, also serves as an articulation of the basic principles of the organization—an indicator of the kind of organization it intends to be and of the scope of goods and services it provides.[51] In addition, the mission statement provides an institution's board of directors, management team physicians, nurses, patients, and the community a sense of the kind of healthcare organization it is and what it is willing to commit itself to do.[52] With a mission statement in place, an organization can measure its fidelity to its self-defining principles. Indeed, external factors such as the expectations of payers and patients, the dynamics of the local market, and a host of other issues all contribute to the concrete manner in which the organization implements its mission and responds to environmental forces. But external factors ought not be the sole determinants of the activities of an organization that strives to maintain its corporate identity. Integrity requires that healthcare organizations not act in an opportunistic manner, but rather align decisions and actions to be consistent with their fundamental missions.[53]

The second value, *responsibility,* is based on the premise that institutions such as hospitals, integrated healthcare systems, insurers, and other healthcare organizations are moral agents. Their actions and failure to act have moral consequences for themselves, patients, and the communities they serve. These organizations should be viewed as "participants in the moral order, as potential objects of moral concern."[54] Traditional medical ethics has focused on the individual physician or caregiver as the relevant moral agent—as an autonomous moral agent with fiduciary duties to individual patients.[55] However, as Reiser[56] and Emanuel[57] have argued, contemporary medical practice occurs within institutionalized structures, within specific policies and procedures. The rules of the game are not determined by individual practitioners in the context of the ad hoc physician-patient relationship. Healthcare institutions can no longer be viewed as innocent, neutral bystanders to the multiple ethical issues associated with American healthcare. This conviction corresponds to Collier's argument that organizational ethics must be based on a theory of moral agency rather than an act-centered approach. "Agent centered ethical theory," she writes, "is concerned with the nature, attributes and potential of the moral agent. . . . [Ethical practice] is rooted in the purposes, judgements and conscience of the moral agent."[58] The mission discernment process is premised upon the conviction that the institution is a moral agent that, through its reflective processes, plans and thus incurs responsibility for its actions. The nature and attributes of the institution as a moral agent are grounded in its reflective, deliberative processes by which it charts its path within an environment. Mission discernment builds upon the basic purpose of the corporation and is itself an essential element in the judgment (that is, the decision-making processes) of the corporation.

The third value, *choice,* is based on the conviction that the healthcare institution is a responsive moral agent. Niebuhr enunciated his theory of moral responsiveness as an alternative to teleological and deontological ethical models.[59] Teleology assesses moral acts in terms of their outcomes—the consequences and results that follow upon a moral decision. Aristotelians, Thomists, and utilitarians are examples of teleologists. In Niebuhr's language, teleological theories construe human acts as associated with "man the maker" and architect of schemes for human betterment. Deontology, on the other hand, determines moral correctness as founded in moral laws or principles. Such laws or principles might be deduced as dictates of practical reason[60] or practical moral reason done from behind a veil of ignorance.[61] Niebuhr suggests that deontology associates moral agency with "man the citizen" who abides by the laws of the state.[62] Niebuhr's model of responsiveness understands the moral agent as "man the answerer," or man engaged in "dialogue," or "man acting in response to actions upon him."[63] This theory of moral agency seems to be most aligned with the decision-making activities of corporations. Rarely do corporations initiate a service or program simply to foster human benefit. Corporations do, however, respond to forces in their environment such as clinical pathways, outcomes studies, technological advances, and financial and market indicators. Following Niebuhr's model, to understand an institution as responsive is to understand it as a moral agent, "which in all its actions answers to action upon it in accordance with its interpretation of such action."[64]

Niebuhr says that the goal of moral reasoning associated with the model of responsiveness is the "fitting." "For the ethics of responsibility, the *fitting* action, the one that fits into a total interaction as response and as anticipation of further response, is alone conducive to the good and alone is right."[65] Healthcare organizations struggle to respond to the needs of patients, to the expectations of various stakeholders, and to advances in clinical medicine. The *fitting* is found within the interpretation of these competing demands upon a corporation; it is found in the identification of what an organization can and cannot do; it is found in the recognition of a decision that is honestly responsive to such demands and congruent with the self-identity of the organization.

Selznick has a similar notion of institutional responsibility. "In short, to be responsive is a way of being responsible. Responsibility runs to an institutional self identity; to those upon whom the institution depends; and to the community whose well-being it affects."[66] He goes on to affirm, "This responsiveness entails reconstruction of the self as well as out reach to others."[67] A central element of the response theory of moral agency is that the agent itself, the institution, is affected and changed by the decisions it makes. A corporation is not what it *says* about itself, but what it *does*. Its identity is ultimately in its actions.

Finally, the fitting response is concrete. It is usually not the perfect good, the ideal response. Much more frequently, the fitting response is recognized in the convergence of possibilities and "natural limitations" that are already pressing upon the awareness of corporate leadership.[68] No corporation, regardless of how responsible it intends to be, can instantaneously remake the social and economic order. The fitting response is incrementalist in its ambitions; it is willing to accept small, pragmatic efforts that over time and with the support of other similar organizations might ameliorate the many ethical issues that beset the U.S. healthcare delivery system.

Although the model of responsiveness is fundamentally process-based, there are important ethical issues to consider regarding the content or outcomes of decisions. Organizations can use various processes of responsiveness (such as lobbying or public relations efforts) in ways that are "strategically defensive and diversionary" or in ways that enhance economic and political power at the expense of other stakeholders.[69] In the name of responsiveness, a corporation can begin to create its own moral universe that defines meaning and value in self-serving terms, as a bastion for corporate purpose and power unfettered by external moral restraints. Responsiveness, whether in the form of mission discernment or any other process, must have a normative grounding by which to judge the content of actions and decisions that emerge from these processes.[70]

Swanson suggests an important source of normative criteria with respect to the values that are directly integrated into decision-making processes such as mission discernment.[71] This model of "value-attuned responsiveness" emphasizes the explicit integration and expansion of values into strategic and policy decision making. The values that are brought into the process of responsiveness include organizational values, but these organizational values must be brought into alignment with a set of broader social values and goals (such as aggregate welfare and justice) that can help the community to flourish.[72] Social values, introduced into the organization in the form of ethical aims, should draw on background theories and principles regarding organizations, morality, and society and compel leaders to question actions that allow the organization to achieve a set of narrow goals while it violates important social or community needs.[73]

The Holy Cross Health System has incorporated this model of moral agency into its mission discernment process. Staff members in the Corporate Development Division support the process in part because the model of ethical thinking it offers is consonant with the manner in which these professionals have been trained to think. The various divisions of a healthcare corporation are constantly monitoring and interpreting developments that might affect the quality of clinical care, market position, and financial performance. The mission discernment process adds what Werhane calls "moral imagination" to these activities, in its conscious consideration of the ethical implications of such measurement.[74] The ethical challenge is to identify the possibilities suggested by market, financial, and clinical indicators and to identify the options that might best preserve and enhance the self-identity of the healthcare organization, adequately address the expectation of stakeholders, and provide for the needs of the community.

A final note on the mission discernment process. It may appear that this process is intended to avoid social evil and, indeed, when an organization might negligently stumble into such a situation, the process should prevent such a negative outcome. However, two more positive outcomes are associated with this process. First, it clarifies the choice between competing goods. Once an organization moves beyond the avoidance of social evil, it is likely to encounter the dilemma of how to select between two or more potentially good opportunities to serve its stakeholders. Such conflicts of commitments are a common feature of life within healthcare organizations.[75] The second positive result, which is really an offshoot of the first one, is that the process enables an organization to identify clearly the rationales for its decisions. It determines that the choices made are aligned with institutional self-identity and the needs of the community and vulnerable populations, and that the organization takes into account the of a decision on relevant stakeholders.

CONCLUSION

We have argued throughout this essay for adopting a definition of organizational ethics in healthcare that embraces three core themes: (1) the creation of structures and processes that promote integrity with respect to core organizational values, (2) identification and the fulfillment of critical institutional responsibilities to stakeholders, (3) and institutional reflection on critical choices with potentially broad organizational implications.

The mission discernment process promotes ethical discourse and deliberation around institutional integrity, responsibility, and choice—an important practice within some Roman Catholic healthcare institutions such as Holy Cross Health System.[76] Healthcare organizations have some important advantages over other institutions with respect to integration of these practices.[77] Hospitals have had many years of experience with ethical discourse in the clinical domain, particularly through the introduction of ethics committees into these organizations.[78] More recently, healthcare organizations, spurred in part by efforts of the Joint Commission on Accreditation of Healthcare Organizations, have developed organizational ethics committees to address issues such as physician conflict of interest or marketing policies.[79] Healthcare organizations have struggled with how to draw on this experience in clinical ethics to promote deliberation on ethical issues in which organizational and clinical considerations intersect.[80] However, a growing number of organizations are recognizing the need to foster this capacity for institutional reflection in the domain of organizational ethics.[81]

Business ethicists can build on this emerging literature in healthcare ethics and the practical experience of institutions such as Holy Cross Health System. We specifically advocate directing greater attention to institutional reflection and the articulation of practices to promote explicit deliberation around organizational values and critical institutional choices. Our emphasis on the mission discernment process is consistent with the writings of other business ethicists and healthcare scholars who recognize the importance of integrating values into strategic planning and decision making through, for example, adopting an enterprise strategy as a means to integrate strategy and ethics,[82] developing a values-attuned decision-making process,[83] or establishing an organizational ethics program within healthcare organizations.[84]

Our emphasis on mission discernment is most closely aligned with the writings of Collier, who is also centrally concerned with the "normative aspects of the organizational decision-making process."[85] Collier notes that moral discourse is at the heart of organizational practices regarding the evaluation of new projects, strategic formulation, and strategic implementation. Without identifying a specific form by which this moral discourse takes place, Collier argues for a "process of moral argumentation" that allows participants who may have different values to deliberate over ethical issues and attempt "to search together for what is right and just in practical situations."[86] This resonates closely with the ethic of responsiveness and its emphasis on finding the "fitting response" in specific situations.

From this perspective, the morality or legitimacy of corporate decision making is found in the outcomes of the decision, as well as in the processes employed to reach a given decision.[87] These processes incorporate important values (such as participation, tolerance, and respect) that reflect the institution's distinctive character, values, and mission.[88] In characterizing the idea of process, Selznick notes: "It contains the whole matrix of values, purposes, and sensibilities that should inform a course of conduct. . . . Therefore process requires the integration of means and ends."[89]

A heightened attention to process will require a disciplined inquiry by ethicists into the nature of collective decision making and consensus,[90] whether this occurs in forums such as ethics committees or among members pulled together to undertake mission discernment. As Collier points out, important tensions are created by bringing diverse internal and external stakeholders into the organizational decision-making process.[91] Collier and others highlight discourse ethics as a potentially valuable "framework within which the normative aspects of decision making in organizations can be analysed."[92] Discourse ethics adopts a point of view consistent with the ethic of responsiveness. Individuals communicate with one another through a process of moral argumentation[93] that moves these participants to "search together for what is right and just in practical situations."[94] Clearly this is a process of both discernment and judgment.

Corporations and healthcare institutions, as moral agents, will increasingly be challenged to take responsibility not only for outcomes, but also for the processes by which these outcomes are achieved. As more and more healthcare organizations come to recognize the significance of organizational ethics and the role played by processes such as mission discernment in fostering integrity and responsibility in institutional choices, we may move closer to realizing Reiser's vision of an era in healthcare "where corporate decision making bearing on the ethos of practice and patient care in healthcare organization can be considered in structured forums in which the multiple values of the institution can be displayed and argued over."[95]

NOTES

This chapter is a version of an article that will appear in *Business Ethics Quarterly*, © 2001, *Business Ethics Quarterly;* used with permission.

1. P. Starr, *The Social Transformation of American Medicine* (New York: Basic Books, 1982).

2. M. Rodwin, *Medicine, Money, and Morals* (New York: Oxford University Press, 1993); E.H. Morreim, *Balancing Act* (Washington, D.C.: Georgetown University Press, 1995).

3. Morreim, see note 2 above.

4. G. Khusf, "Administrative and Organizational Ethics," *HEC Forum* 9, no. 4 (1997): 299-309; R.L. Potter, "From Clinical Ethics to Organizational Ethics: The Second Stage of the Evolution of Bioethics," *Bioethics Forum* 12, no. 2 (1996): 3-12; E.M. Spencer et al., *Organization Ethics in Health Care* (New York: Oxford University Press, 2000); D.F. Thompson, "Hospital Ethics," *Cambridge Quarterly of Healthcare Ethics* 3 (1992): 203-10.

5. B.H. Gray, *The Profit Motive and Patient Care* (Cambridge, Mass.: Harvard University Press, 1991), 3.

6. Morreim, see note 2 above.

7. S.M. Shortell et al., *Remaking Health Care in America* (San Francisco: Jossey-Bass, 1996).

8. Ibid., 151-2.

9. W.R. Scott et al., *Institutional Change and Healthcare Organizations* (Chicago: University of Chicago Press, 2000).

10. S.J. Reiser, "The Ethical Life of Health Care Organizations," *Hastings Center Report* 24, no. 6 (1994): 28-35.

11. L.S. Paine, "Managing for Organizational Integrity," *Harvard Business Review* 72, no. 2 (March-April 1994): 106-17; see also J. Collier, "Theorising the Ethical Organization," *Business Ethics Quarterly* 8, no. 4 (1998): 621-54.

12. E. Emanuel, "On the Need for Institutional Structures Instead of Principles for Individual Cases," *The Journal of Clinical Ethics* 6, no. 4 (1995): 335-8, at 335.

13. R.N. Bellah et al., *The Good Society* (New York: Alfred A. Knopf, 1991).

14. J. Dewey, *Theory of the Moral Life* (New York: Holt, Rinehart and Winston, 1960); H.R. Niebuhr, *The Responsible Self* (New York: Harper & Row, 1963); Paine, see note 11 above; P. Selznick, *The Moral Commonwealth* (Berkeley, Calif.: University of California Press, 1992).

15. R.A. Phillips and J.D. Margolis, "Toward an Ethics of Organizations," *Business Ethics Quarterly* 9, no. 4 (1999): 619-38.

16. Paine, see note 11 above; L.S. Paine, *Leadership, Ethics, and Organizational Integrity* (Chicago: Irwin, 1997); J.C. Collins and J.I.Porras, *Built to Last* (New York: HarperCollins, 1994).

17. See notes 11 and 16 above.

18. Collins and Porras, see note 16 above.

19. Selznick, see note 14 above, p. 244.

20. See note 15 above, p. 631.

21. P. Selznick, *Leadership in Administration* (Berkeley, Calif.: University of California Press, 1957).

22. Thompson, see note 4 above.

23. See notes 4, 10, and 12 above.

24. See, for example, T.L. Beauchamp and J.F. Childress, *Principles of Biomedical Ethics,* 3rd ed. (New York: Oxford University Press, 1989); A.R. Jonsen, M. Siegler, and W.J. Winslade, *Clinical Ethics,* 3rd ed. (New York: McGraw-Hill, 1992).

25. K. Wildes, "Institutional Identity, Integrity, and Conscience," *Kennedy Institute of Ethics Journal* 7, no. 4 (1997): 413.

26. N. Bowie, "Moral Decision-Making and Multinationals," *Business Ethics Quarterly* 1 (1991): 223-32; R.T. DeGeorge, *Competing with Integrity in International Business* (New York: Oxford University Press, 1993); T. Donaldson, *The Ethics of International Business* (New York: Oxford University Press, 1989).

27. J. Orlando, "The Fourth Wave: The Ethics of Corporate Downsizing," *Business Ethics Quarterly* 9, no. 2 (1999): 295-314; G.W. Watson et al., "Ideology and the Economic Social Contract in a Downsizing Environment," *Business Ethics Quarterly* 9, no. 4 (1999): 659-72.

28. R.E. Freeman, *Strategic Management: A Stakeholder Approach* (Englewood Cliffs, N.J.: Prentice Hall, 1984); T. Donaldson and L. Preston, "The Stakeholder Theory of the Corporation: Concepts, Evidence, Implications," *Academy of Management Review* 20 (1995): 65-91; T.M. Jones and A.C. Wicks, "Convergent Stakeholder Theory," *Academy of Management Review* 24, no. 2 (1999): 206-21.

29. Spencer et al., see note 4 above.

30. Niebuhr, see note 14 above; Selznick, note 14 above.

31. Collier, see note 11 above; Spencer et al., see note 4 above.

32. Niebuhr, see note 14 above.

33. Selznick, see note 14 above, p. 239.

34. For the classic statement, see J. Ladd, "Morality and the Ideal of Rationality in Formal Organizations," *The Monist* (1970): 54.

35. T. Donaldson and P.H. Werhane, eds., *Ethical Issues in Business* (Englewood Cliffs, N.J.: Prentice Hall, 1988); P.A. French, *Collective and Corporate Responsibility* (New York: Columbia University Press, 1984); P.A. French, J. Nesteruk, and D.T. Risser, *Corporations in the Moral Community* (Fort Worth, Tex.: Harcourt Brace Jovanovich, 1992); K.E. Goodpaster and J.B. Matthews, Jr., "Can a Corporation Have a Conscience?" in *Ethical Issues in Business,* ed. T. Donaldson and P.H. Werhane (Englewood Cliffs, N.J.: Prentice Hall, 1988), 139-48; L. May, *The Morality of Groups* (Notre Dame, Ind.: University of Notre Dame Press, 1987).

36. Collier, see note 11 above, p. 646.

37. D.L. Swanson, "Addressing a Theoretical Problem by Reorienting the Corporate Social Performance Model," *Academy of Management Review* 20, no. 2 (1995): 43-58.

38. Collier, see note 11 above.

39. Selznick, see note 14 above, p. 338.

40. Collier, see note 11 above; Spencer et al., see note 4 above.

41. Collier, see note 11 above.

42. See note 37 above.

43. T. Donaldson and T. Dunfee, *Ties That Bind: A Social Contracts Approach to Business Ethics* (Boston: Harvard University Business School Press, 1999).

44. D.L. Swanson, "Toward an Integrative Theory of Business and Society: A Research Strategy for Corporate Social Performance," *Academy of Management Review* 24, no. 3 (1999): 506-21.

45. Selznick, see note 14 above.

46. Donaldson and Preston, see note 28 above.

47. See notes 43 and 44 above.

48. D.R. Conner, *Managing at the Speed of Change* (New York: Villard Books, 1992).

49. See note 15 above, pp. 627-8.

50. Selznick, see note 14 above, p. 276.

51. Collins and Porras, see note 16 above.

52. Spencer et al., see note 4 above.

53. Selznick, see notes 14 and 21 above.

54. Selznick, see note 14 above, p. 231.

55. See note 24 above.

56. See note 10 above.

57. See note 12 above.

58. Collier, see note 11 above, p. 625.

59. Niebuhr, see note 14 above.

60. I. Kant, *Critique of Practical Reason,* trans. L.W. Beck (Indianapolis: Bobbs-Merrill, 1956).

61. J. Rawls, *A Theory of Justice* (Cambridge, Mass.: Harvard University Press, 1971).

62. Niebuhr, see note 14 above.

63. Ibid., 56.

64. Ibid., 57.

65. Ibid., 61.

66. Selznick, see note 14 above, p. 338.

67. Ibid.

68. See note 15 above, p. 631.

69. See note 37 above, pp. 47-8.

70. Ibid.

71. Swanson, see note 44 above.

72. Ibid.; see note 43 above.

73. N. Daniels, "Wide Reflective Equilibrium and Theory Acceptance in Ethics," *Journal of Philosophy* 76, no. 5 (1979): 256-83; see notes 43 and 61 above; see note 15 above.

74. P.H. Werhane, "Moral Imagination and the Search for Ethical Decision Making in Management," *Business Ethics Quarterly* (special issue, no. 1) (1998): 81-5.

75. Spencer et al., see note 4 above.

76. B.W. Meyer, "Ensuring Accountability in Decision-Making," *Health Progress* (May-June 1997): 30-2; J.T. Tuohey, "Covenant Model of Corporate Compliance," *Health Progress* (July-August 1998): 70-5.

77. See note 10 above.

78. For an in-depth discussion of the growth of institutional ethics committees in healthcare, see J.D. Moreno, *Deciding Together* (New York: Oxford University Press, 1995).

79. P.M. Schyve, "Patient Rights and Organization Ethics: The Joint Commission Perspective," *Bioethics Forum* 12, no. 2 (1996): 13-20; L.J. Weber, "Taking on Organizational Ethics," *Health Progress* (May-June 1997): 20-3, 32.

80. See note 10 above.

81. Khusf, see note 4 above; Potter, see note 4 above; Thompson, see note 4 above.

82. R.E. Freeman and D.R. Gilbert, *Corporate Strategy and the Search for Ethics* (Englewood Cliffs, N.J.: Prentice Hall, 1988).

83. Swanson, see note 44 above.

84. Spencer et al., see note 4 above.

85. Collier, see note 11 above, p. 633.

86. Ibid., 642.

87. Freeman and Gilbert, see note 82 above; T.M. Jones and L.D. Goldberg, "Governing the Large Corporation: More Arguments for Public Directors," *Academy of Management Review* 20 (1982): 404-37; Swanson, see notes 37 and 44 above.

88. Selznick, see note 14 above; Swanson, see note 44 above.

89. Selznick, see note 14 above, p. 331.

90. See note 78 above.

91. Collier, see note 11 above.

92. Ibid., 642; see also Swanson, note 44 above; D.F. Thompson, *Discourse and Knowledge* (London: Routledge, 1998).

93. Collier, see note 11 above; J. Habermas, *Moral Consciousness and Communicative Action,* trans. C. Lenhardt and S.W. Nicholson (Cambridge, Mass.: MIT Press, 1991); Thompson, see note 92 above.

94. Collier, see note 11 above.

95. S.J. Reiser, "Hospitals as Humane Corporations," in *Integrity in Health Care Institutions: Humane Environments for Teaching, Inquiry, and Healing,* ed. R.E. Bulger and S.J. Reiser (Iowa City, Iowa: University of Iowa Press, 1990), 121-9.

Appendix F-1
Codes of Ethics

Principles of Medical Ethics

American Medical Association

The medical profession has long subscribed to a body of ethical statements developed primarily for the benefit of the patient. As a member of this profession, a physician must recognize responsibility not only to patients, but also to society, to other health professionals, and to self. The following principles adopted by the American Medical Association are not laws, but standards of conduct, which define the essentials of honorable behavior for the physician.

I. A physician shall be dedicated to providing competent medical service with compassion and respect for human dignity.

II. A physician shall deal honestly with patients and colleagues, and strive to expose those physicians deficient in character or competence, or who engage in fraud or deception.

III. A physician shall respect the law and also recognize a responsibility to seek changes in those requirements which are contrary to the best interests of the patient.

IV. A physician shall respect the rights of patients, of colleagues, and of other health professionals, and shall safeguard patient confidences within the constraints of the law.

V. A physician shall continue to study, apply, and advance scientific knowledge, make relevant information available to patients, colleagues, and the public, obtain consultation, and use the talent of other health professionals when indicated

VI. A physician shall, in the provision of appropriate patient care, except in emergencies, be free to choose whom to serve, with whom to associate, and the environment in which to provide medical services

VII. A physician shall recognize a responsibility to participate in activities contributing to an improved community.

Code of Medical Ethics: Current Opinions with Annotations, American Medical Association, © 2000; used with its kind permission. Source: <http://www.ama-assn.org/ethic/ceja/pome.htm>.

Appendix F-2

Code of Ethics for Nurses

American Nurses Association

Working Draft 9
Revised 7 June 2000

1. The nurse, in all professional relationships, practices with compassion and respect for the inherent dignity, worth and uniqueness of every individual, unrestricted by considerations of social or economic status, personal attributes, or the nature of health problems. . . .

2. The nurse's primary commitment is to the patient, whether an individual, family, group or community. . . .

3. The nurse promotes, advocates for and strives to protect the health, safety and rights of the patient. . . .

4. The nurse is responsible and accountable for individual nursing practice and determines the appropriate delegation of tasks consistent with the nurse's obligation to provide optimum patient care. . . .

5. The nurse owes the same duties to self as to others, including the responsibility to preserve integrity and safety, to maintain competence and to continue personal and professional growth. . . .

6. The nurse participates in establishing, maintaining and improving healthcare environments and conditions of employment conducive to the provision of quality healthcare and consistent with the values of the profession through individual and collective action. . . .

7. The nurse participates in the advancement of the profession through contributions to practice, education, administration, and knowledge development. . . .

8. The nurse collaborates with other health professionals and the public in promoting community, national, and international efforts to meet health needs. . . .

9. The profession of nursing, as represented by associates and their members, is responsible for articulating nursing values, for maintaining

the integrity of the profession and its practice and for shaping social policy. . . .

Code of Ethics for Nurses, American Nurses Association, © 2001; used with its kind permission. Source: <http://www.ana.org/ethics/#3>.

Appendix F-3

Code of Ethics

Healthcare Information and Management Systems Society

PREFACE

The Healthcare Information and Management Systems Society is a membership organization, and, as such, undertakes efforts to inform, educate, and support the professional enhancement of the membership through publications, conferences, meetings, or other organized events, either solely sponsored by HIMSS or jointly with other organizations. Because of the diversity of interests and businesses represented by the membership, this Code of Ethics is designed to serve as a guide for the personal and professional conduct of the Society and its members in order to avoid any potential allegations of unethical conduct and to outline a procedure to investigate and resolve these allegations. Members have an obligation to act in ways that will merit the trust, confidence, and respect of their professional peers, the general public, other professional organizations and the health care industry in general. Individual acts that transgress from this Code of Ethics will not be condoned.

I. RESPONSIBILITIES OF MEMBERS

1. Uphold the values, ethics, and mission of the profession and the Society;
2. Conduct all personal and professional activities with honesty, integrity, respect, fairness, and good faith in a manner that will reflect well on the profession and the Society;
3. Comply with all laws and regulations in the jurisdictions in which the member is located or conducts professional and personal activities;
4. Maintain competence and proficiency in their profession by un-

dertaking a personal program of assessment and continuing professional education;

5. Avoid the exploitation of professional relationships or positions in the Society, either elected or appointed, for personal gain;

6. Use this Code to further the interests of the profession and not for personal selfish reasons;

7. Respect professional confidences;

8. Enhance the dignity and image of the profession and the Society through positive personal actions;

9. Refrain from participating in any activity that demeans the credibility and dignity of any professional peer, member of the Society, or the Society itself;

10. Refrain from using membership or association with the Society to promote or endorse external products or services;

11. Be truthful in all forms of professional and organizational communications and avoid information that is false, misleading, inflammatory, and deceptive, or information that would create unreasonable expectations;

12. Accept no gifts or benefits offered with the expectation of influencing a decision when conducting business on behalf of the Society.

Code of Ethics, Healthcare Information and Management System Society, © 2001; used with its kind permission. Source: <www.himss.org>; HIMSS, 230 East Ohio Street, Suite 500, Chicago, Illinois 60611.

Appendix F-4

Consensus Statement on the Ethic of Medicine

Council of Medical Specialty Societies

25 April 1998
Reaffirmed 20 November 1999

PREAMBLE

The practice of medicine is rooted in a covenant of trust among patients, physicians and society. The ethic of medicine must seek to balance the physicians' responsibility to each patient and the professional, collective obligation to all who need medical care.

This statement articulates core values and principles that are shared by all physicians, in a range of settings and circumstances, including the use of new technologies of communication, regardless of specialty.

THE PHYSICIAN-PATIENT RELATIONSHIP

1. The physician's primary, inviolate role is as an active advocate for each patient's care and well-being.

2. The physician should treat each patient with honesty, compassion, dignity, and respect for individual autonomy.

3. The physician's commitment to patients includes health education and continuity of care.

THE PHYSICIAN-PHYSICIAN RELATIONSHIP

1. Physicians have a responsibility to maintain moral integrity, intellectual honesty, and clinical competence.

2. Physicians, as stewards of medical knowledge, have an obliga-

tion to educate and share information with colleagues, including physicians-in-training.

THE RELATIONSHIP OF THE PHYSICIAN TO SYSTEMS OF CARE

1. The physician's duty of patient advocacy should not be altered by the system of health care delivery in which the physician practices.

2. Physicians should resolve conflicts of interest in a fashion that gives primacy to the patient's interests.

3. Physicians should provide knowledgeable input into organizational decisions on the allocation of medical resources and the process of health care delivery.

THE RELATIONSHIP OF THE PHYSICIAN TO SOCIETY

1. Physicians have a responsibility to serve the health care needs of all members of society.

2. Physicians have an ethical obligation to participate in the formation of health care policy.

3. Physicians have an ethical obligation to preserve and protect the trust bestowed on them by society.

CLOSING

Some of the values and principles that impinge on the relationship of physicians to their patients, colleagues, organizations, and the larger society in which they practice are introduced in this document. Further specifications can be developed to fit the particular needs of individual specialties, patient groups, and practice circumstances.

Consensus Statement on the Ethic of Medicine, Council of Medical Specialties Societies, © 2001; used with its kind permission. Source: <http://www.cmss.org/consensus.html>.

Appendix F-5

Declaration of Helsinki Recommendations Guiding Medical Doctors in Biomedical Research Involving Human Subjects

World Medical Association

Adopted by the 18th World Medical Association General Assembly, Helsinki, Finland, June 1964
Amended by the 29th World Medical Association General Assembly, Tokyo, Japan, October 1975,
35th World Medical Association General Assembly, Venice, Italy, October 1983,
41st World Medical Association General Assembly, Hong Kong, September 1989,
48th World Medical Association General Assembly, Somerset West, Republic of South Africa, October 1996,
52nd World Medical Association General Assembly, Edinburgh, Scotland, October 2000

A. INTRODUCTION

1. The World Medical Association has developed the Declaration of Helsinki as a statement of ethical principles to provide guidance to physicians and other participants in medical research involving human subjects. Medical research involving human subjects includes research on identifiable human material or identifiable data.

2. It is the duty of the physician to promote and safeguard the health of the people. The physician's knowledge and conscience are dedicated to the fulfillment of this duty.

3. The Declaration of Geneva of the World Medical Association binds the physician with the words, "The health of my patient will be my first consideration," and the International Code of Medical Ethics declares that, "A physician shall act only in the patient's interest when providing medical care which might have the effect of weakening the physical and mental condition of the patient."

4. Medical progress is based on research which ultimately must rest in part on experimentation involving human subjects.

5. In medical research on human subjects, considerations related to the well-being of the human subject should take precedence over the interests of science and society.

6. The primary purpose of medical research involving human subjects is to improve prophylactic, diagnostic, and therapeutic procedures and the understanding of the aetiology and pathogenesis of disease. Even the best proven prophylactic, diagnostic, and therapeutic methods must continuously be challenged through research for their effectiveness, efficiency, accessibility, and quality.

7. In current medical practice and in medical research, most prophylactic, diagnostic, and therapeutic procedures involve risks and burdens.

8. Medical research is subject to ethical standards that promote respect for all human beings and protect their health and rights. Some research populations are vulnerable and need special protection. The particular needs of the economically and medically disadvantaged must be recognized. Special attention is also required for those who cannot give or refuse consent for themselves, for those who may be subject to giving consent under duress, for those who will not benefit personally from the research, and for those for whom the research is combined with care.

9. Research investigators should be aware of the ethical, legal, and regulatory requirements for research on human subjects in their own countries as well as applicable international requirements. No national ethical, legal, or regulatory requirement should be allowed to reduce or eliminate any of the protections for human subjects set forth in this Declaration.

B. BASIC PRINCIPLES FOR ALL MEDICAL RESEARCH

10. It is the duty of the physician in medical research to protect the life, health, privacy, and dignity of the human subject.

11. Medical research involving human subjects must conform to generally accepted scientific principles, be based on a thorough knowledge of the scientific literature, other relevant sources of information,

and on adequate laboratory and, where appropriate, animal experimentation.

12. Appropriate caution must be exercised in the conduct of research which may affect the environment, and the welfare of animals used for research must be respected.

13. The design and performance of each experimental procedure involving human subjects should be clearly formulated in an experimental protocol. This protocol should be submitted for consideration, comment, guidance, and, where appropriate, approval to a specially appointed ethical review committee, which must be independent of the investigator, the sponsor or any other kind of undue influence. This independent committee should be in conformity with the laws and regulations of the country in which the research experiment is performed. The committee has the right to monitor ongoing trials. The researcher has the obligation to provide monitoring information to the committee, especially any serious adverse events. The researcher should also submit to the committee, for review, information regarding funding, sponsors, institutional affiliations, other potential conflicts of interest and incentives for subjects.

14. The research protocol should always contain a statement of the ethical considerations involved and should indicate that there is compliance with the principles enunciated in this Declaration.

15. Medical research involving human subjects should be conducted only by scientifically qualified persons and under the supervision of a clinically competent medical person. The responsibility for the human subject must always rest with a medically qualified person and never rest on the subject of the research, even though the subject has given consent.

16. Every medical research project involving human subjects should be preceded by careful assessment of predictable risks and burdens in comparison with foreseeable benefits to the subject or to others. This does not preclude the participation of healthy volunteers in medical research. The design of all studies should be publicly available.

17. Physicians should abstain from engaging in research projects involving human subjects unless they are confident that the risks involved have been adequately assessed and can be satisfactorily managed. Physicians should cease any investigation if the risks are found to outweigh the potential benefits or if there is conclusive proof of positive and beneficial results.

18. Medical research involving human subjects should only be conducted if the importance of the objective outweighs the inherent risks and burdens to the subject. This is especially important when the human subjects are healthy volunteers.

19. Medical research is only justified if there is a reasonable likelihood that the populations in which the research is carried out stand to benefit from the results of the research.

20. The subjects must be volunteers and informed participants in the research project.

21. The right of research subjects to safeguard their integrity must always be respected. Every precaution should be taken to respect the privacy of the subject, the confidentiality of the patient's information, and to minimize the impact of the study on the subject's physical and mental integrity and on the personality of the subject.

22. In any research on human beings, each potential subject must be adequately informed of the aims, methods, sources of funding, any possible conflicts of interest, institutional affiliations of the researcher, the anticipated benefits and potential risks of the study, and the discomfort it may entail. The subject should be informed of the right to abstain from participation in the study or to withdraw consent to participate at any time without reprisal. After ensuring that the subject has understood the information, the physician should then obtain the subject's freely-given informed consent, preferably in writing. If the consent cannot be obtained in writing, the non-written consent must be formally documented and witnessed.

23. When obtaining informed consent for the research project the physician should be particularly cautious if the subject is in a dependent relationship with the physician or may consent under duress. In that case the informed consent should be obtained by a well-informed physician who is not engaged in the investigation and who is completely independent of this relationship.

24. For a research subject who is legally incompetent, physically or mentally incapable of giving consent, or is a legally incompetent minor, the investigator must obtain informed consent from the legally authorized representative in accordance with applicable law. These groups should not be included in research unless the research is necessary to promote the health of the population represented and this research cannot instead be performed on legally competent persons.

25. When a subject deemed legally incompetent, such as a minor child, is able to give assent to decisions about participation in research, the investigator must obtain that assent in addition to the consent of the legally authorized representative.

26. Research on individuals from whom it is not possible to obtain consent, including proxy or advance consent, should be done only if the physical/mental condition that prevents obtaining informed consent is a necessary characteristic of the research population. The specific reasons for involving research subjects with a condition that renders them unable to give informed consent should be stated in the ex-

perimental protocol for consideration and approval of the review committee. The protocol should state that consent to remain in the research should be obtained as soon as possible from the individual or a legally authorized surrogate.

27. Both authors and publishers have ethical obligations. In publication of the results of research, the investigators are obliged to preserve the accuracy of the results. Negative as well as positive results should be published or otherwise publicly available. Sources of funding, institutional affiliations, and any possible conflicts of interest should be declared in the publication. Reports of experimentation not in accordance with the principles laid down in this Declaration should not be accepted for publication.

C. ADDITIONAL PRINCIPLES FOR MEDICAL RESEARCH COMBINED WITH MEDICAL CARE

28. The physician may combine medical research with medical care, only to the extent that the research is justified by its potential prophylactic, diagnostic, or therapeutic value. When medical research is combined with medical care, additional standards apply to protect the patients who are research subjects.

29. The benefits, risks, burdens, and effectiveness of a new method should be tested against those of the best current prophylactic, diagnostic, and therapeutic methods. This does not exclude the use of placebo, or no treatment, in studies where no proven prophylactic, diagnostic, or therapeutic method exists.

30. At the conclusion of the study, every patient entered into the study should be assured of access to the best proven prophylactic, diagnostic, and therapeutic methods identified by the study.

31. The physician should fully inform the patient which aspects of the care are related to the research. The refusal of a patient to participate in a study must never interfere with the patient-physician relationship.

32. In the treatment of a patient, where proven prophylactic, diagnostic, and therapeutic methods do not exist or have been ineffective, the physician, with informed consent from the patient, must be free to use unproven or new prophylactic, diagnostic and therapeutic measures, if in the physician's judgement it offers hope of saving life, re-establishing health, or alleviating suffering. Where possible, these measures should be made the object of research, designed to evaluate their safety and efficacy. In all cases, new information should be recorded and, where appropriate, published. The other relevant guidelines of this Declaration should be followed.

Declaration of Helsinki, World Medical Association, © 2001; used with its kind permission. Source: The World Medical Association, Inc., PO Box 63, 01212 Ferney-Voltaire Cedex, France. Phone: +33 4 50 40 75 75. Fax: +33 4 50 40 59 37. E-mail: <info@wma.net>.

Appendix F-6

Code of Ethics

American College of Healthcare Executives

As Amended by the Council of Regents at its Annual Meeting
22 August 1995

PREAMBLE

The purpose of the Code of Ethics of the American College of Health-care Executives is to serve as a guide to conduct its members. It contains standards of ethical behavior for healthcare executives in their professional relationships. These relationships include members of the healthcare executive's organization and other organizations. Also included are patients or others served, colleagues, the community, and society as a whole. The Code of Ethics also incorporates standards of ethical behavior governing personal behavior, particularly when that conduct directly relates to the role and identity of the healthcare executive.

The fundamental objectives of the healthcare management profession are to enhance overall quality of life, dignity, and well-being of every individual needing healthcare services; and to create a more equitable, accessible, effective, and efficient healthcare system.

In fulfilling their commitments and obligations to patients or others served, healthcare executives function as moral advocates. Since every management decision affects the health and well-being of both individuals and communities, healthcare executives must carefully evaluate the possible outcomes of their decisions. In organizations that deliver healthcare services, they must work to safeguard and foster rights, interests, and prerogatives of patients or others served. The role of moral advocate requires that healthcare executives speak out and take actions necessary to promote such rights, interests, and prerogatives if they are threatened.

I. THE HEALTHCARE EXECUTIVE'S RESPONSIBILITIES TO THE PROFESSION OF HEALTHCARE MANAGEMENT

The healthcare executive shall:

A. Uphold the values, ethics, and mission of the healthcare management profession;

B. Conduct all personal and professional activities with honesty, integrity, respect, fairness, and good faith in a manner that will reflect well upon the profession;

C. Comply with all laws pertaining to healthcare management in the jurisdiction in which the healthcare executive is located, or conducts professional activities;

D. Maintain competence and efficiency in healthcare management by implementing a personal program of assessment and continuing professional education;

E. Avoid the exploitation of professional relationships for personal gain;

F. Use this Code to further the interests of the profession and not for selfish reasons;

G. Respect professional confidences;

H. Enhance the dignity and image of the healthcare management profession through positive public information programs; and

I. Refrain from participating in any activity that demeans the credibility and dignity of the healthcare management profession.

II. THE HEALTHCARE EXECUTIVE'S RESPONSIBILITIES TO PATIENTS OR OTHERS SERVED, TO THE ORGANIZATION, AND TO EMPLOYEES

A. Responsibilities to patients or others served

The healthcare executive shall, within the scope of his or her authority:

1. Work to ensure the existence of a process to evaluate the quality of care or service rendered;

2. Avoid practicing or facilitating discrimination and institute safeguards to prevent discriminatory organizational practices;

3. Work to ensure the existence of a process that will advise patients or others served of the rights, opportunities, responsibilities, and risks regarding available healthcare services;

4. Work to provide a process that ensures the autonomy and self-determination of patients or others served; and

5. Work to ensure the existence of procedures that will safeguard the confidentiality and privacy of patients or others served.

B. Responsibility to the organization

The healthcare executive shall, within the scope of his or her authority:

1. Provide healthcare services consistent with available resources and work to ensure the existence of a resource allocation process that considers ethical ramifications;

2. Conduct both competitive and cooperative activities in ways that improve community healthcare services;

3. Lead the organization in the use and improvement of standards of management and sound business practices;

4. Respect the customs and practices of patients or others served, consistent with the organization's philosophy; and

5. Be truthful in all forms of professional and organizational communication, and avoid disseminating information that is false, misleading, or deceptive.

C. Responsibilities to employees

Healthcare executives have an ethical and professional obligation to employees of the organizations they manage that encompass but are not limited to:

1. Working to create a working environment conducive for underscoring employee ethical conduct and behavior;

2. Working to ensure that individuals may freely express ethical concerns and providing mechanisms for discussing and addressing such concerns;

3. Working to ensure a working environment that is free from harassment, sexual and other; coercion of any kind, especially to perform illegal or unethical acts; and discrimination on the basis of race, creed, color, sex, ethnic origin, age, or disability;

4. Working to ensure a working environment that is conducive to proper utilization of employees' skills and abilities;

5. Paying particular attention to the employee's work environment and job safety; and

6. Working to establish appropriate grievance and appeals mechanisms.

III. CONFLICTS OF INTEREST

A conflict of interest may be only a matter of degree, but exists when the healthcare executive:

A. Acts to benefit directly or indirectly by using authority or inside information or allows a friend, relative, or associate to benefit from such authority or information.

B. Uses authority or information to make a decision to intentionally affect the organization in an adverse manner.

The healthcare executive shall:

A. Conduct all personal and professional relationships in such a way that all those affected are assured that management decisions are made in the best interest of the organization and the individuals served by it;

B. Disclose to the appropriate authorities any direct or indirect financial or personal interests that pose potential or actual conflicts of interest;

C. Accept no gifts or benefits offered with the express or implied expectation of influencing a management decision; and

D. Inform the appropriate authority and other involved parties of potential or actual conflicts of interest related to appointments or elections to boards or committees inside our outside the healthcare executive's organization.

IV. THE HEALTHCARE EXECUTIVE'S RESPONSIBILITY TO COMMUNITY AND SOCIETY

The healthcare executive shall:

A. Work to identify and meet the healthcare needs of the community;

B. Work to ensure that all people have reasonable access to healthcare services;

C. Participate in public dialogue on healthcare policy issues and advocate solutions that will improve health status and promote quality healthcare;

D. Consider the short-term and long-term impact of management decisions on both the community and on society; and

E. Provide prospective consumers with adequate and accurate information, enabling them to make enlightened judgments and decisions regarding services.

V. THE HEALTHCARE EXECUTIVE'S RESPONSIBILITY TO REPORT VIOLATIONS OF THE CODE

A member of the College who has reasonable grounds to believe that another member has violated this Code has a duty to communicate such facts to the Ethics Committee.

Code of Ethics, American College of Healthcare Executives, © 2001; used with its kind permission. Source: <http://www.ache.org/code.html>.

Contributors

JUDITH ANDRE, PHD, is a Professor of Philosophy at the Center for Ethics and Humanities in the Life Sciences at Michigan State University in East Lansing.

CARRINGTON L. BAILEY, DMIN, is Manager for Spiritual Care at Medicorp Healthsystem in Fredericksburg, Virginia.

MYRA J. CHRISTOPHER is President and CEO of the Midwest Bioethics Center; and is Program Director of Community-State Partnerships to Improve End-of-Life Care in Kansas City, Missouri.

WALTER A. DAVIS, MD, MA, is Director of Education at the Center for Biomedical Ethics at the University of Virginia School of Medicine in Charlottesville.

PATRICIA DONEHOWER, MSN, RN, is Director of Adult Home Care at the Visiting Nurse Association in Burlington, Vermont.

JAMES J. FINNERTY, MD, MA, is an Assistant Professor in the Department Ob/Gyn at the University of Virginia School of Medicine in Charlottesville.

CATHY FRANK, MAT, is Chair of the Board of Trustees Ethics Committee at Fletcher Allen Health Care in Burlington, Vermont.

CHRISTOPHER W. FUERST, RRT, RN, is a Clinician II in the Medical Intensive-Care Unit; and is a Clinical Associate at the Center for Biomedical Ethics at the University of Virginia School of Medicine in Charlottesville.

AMANDA BETH FULMOR, BA, is an Associate Consultant at Bain and Company in Atlanta, Georgia.

JOHN A. GALLAGHER, PHD, is Director of the Center for Ethics in Health Care at Saint Joseph Health System in Atlanta, Georgia.

JERRY GOODSTEIN, PHD, is an Associate Professor in the Department of Managment and Decision Sciences at Washington State University in Vancouver.

CYNTHIA M. JORDAN, MDIV, is Director of Pastoral Care at Catawba Memorial Hospital in Catawba, North Carolina.

SUSAN E. KENNEL, MSN, RN CPNP, is an Assistant Professor at the University of Virginia School of Nursing in Charlottesville.

LINDA J. KEILMAN, RN, CS, MSN, is an Assistant Professor/Geriatric Nurse Practitioner in the College of Nursing at Michigan State University in East Lansing.

PAUL A. LOMBARDO, PHD, JD, is Director of the Program in Law and Medicine at the Center for Biomedical Ethics at the University of Virginia School of Medicine in Charlottesville.

SUE McCOY, MD, PHD, FACS, is a Professor of Surgery at the James H. Quillen College of Medicine at East Tennessee State University in Johnson City.

ANN E. MILLS, MSC (ECON), MBA, is Associate Director of Outreach Programs at the Center for Biomedical Ethics at the University of Virginia School of Medicine in Charlottesville.

JONATHAN D. MORENO, PHD, is Kornfeld Professor of Biomedical Ethics; and is Director of the Center for Biomedical Ethics at the University of Virginia School of Medicine in Charlottesville.

JOAN L. MURRAY, MN, DMIN, is Director of Pastoral Education in the Department of Chaplaincy Services and Pastoral Education at the University of Virginia Health System in Charlottesville.

CATHERINE MYSER, PHD, is Director of the Ethics Program of the University of Vermont College of Medicine/Fletcher Allen Health Care in Burlington, Vermont.

BETTY L. NEWELL, MA, is a Member of the University of Virginia Organization Ethics Committee in Charlottesville.

PHILLIP NIEBURG, MD, MPH, is Associate Director for Science at the National Center for HIV, STD, and TB Prevention at the Centers for Disease Control and Prevention in Atlanta, Georgia.

BRIAN O'TOOLE, PHD, is Vice President for Mission and Ethics at the Sisters of Mercy Health System in Saint Louis, Missouri.

ROBERT L. POTTER, MD, PHD, is Ethics Scholar at the Midwest Bioethics Center in Kansas City, Missouri.

PATRICIA REAMS, MD, MPH, is a Pediatrician at the Educational Institute for Cumberland at Brown Schools Hospital for Children and Adolescents in New Kent, Virginia.

CHRISTY A. RENTMEESTER, MA, is a Graduate Student in the Department of Philosophy at Michigan State University in East Lansing.

MARY V. RORTY, PHD, MA, is a Clinical Associate Professor at Stanford University School of Medicine in Stanford, California.

MARGARET L. SKELLEY IS Director of the Office of the Chief of Staff at the University of Virginia in Charlottesville.

EDWARD M. SPENCER, MD, is Director of Outreach Programs at the Center for Biomedical Ethics at the University of Virginia School of Medicine in Charlottesville.

BETHANY SPIELMAN, PhD, JD, is an Associate Professor in the Department of Medical Humanities at Southern Illinois University School of Medicine in Springfield.

FREEMAN SUBER, MD, MA, is a Postdoctoral Medical Fellow at Dartmouth College; and is a Member of the Ethics Committee at Dartmouth-Hitchcock Medical Center in Hanover, New Hampshire.

WILLIAM T. WARMATH is Director of Patient Relations; and is a Patient Advocate and Counselor at the Moses Cone Health System in Greensboro, North Carolina.

ROBERT D. WELLS, PhD, is Director of Ethics and Research at Valley Children's Hospital; and is an Associate Clinical Professor of Pediatrics and Psychiatry at the University of California—San Francisco.

PATRICIA H. WERHANE, PhD, is Ruffin Professor of Business Ethics; and is Senior Fellow at the Olsson Center for Applied Ethics at the Darden Graduate School of Business Administration at the University of Virginia in Charlottesville.

JULIA MILNER WEST, MSW, is Ethics Consultant/Ethics Coordinator at Sentara Center for Healthcare Ethics; and is Co-Chair of the Sentara Ethics Advisory Council at Sentara Healthcare in Norfolk, Virginia.

EARL D. WHITE, II, MD, is Chairman of the Sentara Hampton General Hospital Ethics Committee; is Co-Chair of the Sentara Ethics Advisory Council; is an Ethics Consultant; and is a Practicing Orthopedic Surgeon at Sentara Hampton General Hospital in Norfolk, Virginia.